FORESTRY COMMISSION BULLETIN 115

Alternative Silvicultural Systems to Clear Cutting in Britain: A Review

Cyril Hart

D1613281

LONDON : HMSO

ISBN 0 11 710334 9

Hart, C.; 1995. Alternative Silvicultural Systems to Clear Cutting in Britain: A Review. Bulletin 115, HMSO, London. xiv + 101pp.

FDC 22: 221.1: (410): (4)

KEYWORDS: Amenity, Broadleaves, Conifers, Conservation, Establishment, Forestry, Management

---

Cyril Hart

Dr Cyril Hart OBE is a Chartered Surveyor and Chartered Forester and is the Queen's Senior Verderer for the Forest of Dean. He is author of several books on Britain's forests and trees of which the best known is his authoritative *Practical forestry for the agent and surveyor*.

Professor Julian Evans and Mr Gary Kerr of the Forestry Commission's Research Division contributed to this important review through editorial involvement and text revision.

Front cover: Weasenham New Wood, Norfolk: mixed conifer selection system; in the picture, Major Richard Coke DSO MC, the present owner.
(PETER GOODWIN)

Back cover: Dr Cyril Hart OBE
(DAVID GREEN)

Please address enquiries about this publication to:
Research Publications Officer
The Forestry Commission
Research Division
Alice Holt Lodge, Wrecclesham
Farnham, Surrey GU10 4LH

WITHDRAWN

Acknowledgements

This Bulletin was written with the benefit of Professor J.D. Matthews's updating (1989) of Professor R.S. Troup's two editions of *Silvicultural systems* (1928, 1952), the latter edition by Dr E.W. Jones. Eminently rewarding too has been co-operation received from David Paterson, recently retired from the Forestry Commission, whose publications and erudite comments, based on a wide experience of practice and research in silviculture, have been invaluable. Likewise acknowledged are texts of Professor M.L. Anderson, and of Forestry Commission staff, in particular: Julian Evans, John Everard OBE, Gary Kerr, Mark Yorke and Adrian Whiteman. Additional assistance relating to silvicultural systems was received directly or indirectly from Simon Bell, John Blyth, Paul Bond, Graham Booth, Richard Broadhurst, Robert Budden, Vernon Daykin, Christine Cahalan, Murray Carter, Lord Cawdor, Major Richard Coke, Wilfred Fox, Bob Furness, Michael Gane, Ted Garfitt, Peter Garthwaite OBE, David Goss, Sandy Greig, Michael Harley OBE, Esmond Harris, Anthony Hart, Rodney Helliwell, Paul Hill-Tout, Peter Hughes, Phillip Hutt MBE, Robert Jordan, Talis Kalnars, Felix Karthaus, Steve Lee, Arthur Lloyd, Roy Lorrain-Smith, David Lowe, John MacKenzie, Douglas Malcolm OBE, John McHardy, Robert McIntosh, Philippe Morgan, Andrew Neustein, John Newcomb, Trefor Owen, Colin Price, Chris Quine, Michael Reade DSC, John Robinson, Martin Rogers, Irvine Ross, Roddy Ross, Robin Satow, Derek Stickler, Ken Stott, Charles Taylor, David Taylor, Keith Wallis, Guy Watt, Michael Wemyss, Helen Whitney McIver, John Workman OBE, and Richard Worrell. References to many of them are made in the text. For useful comments and editorial assistance throughout I thank Jenny Claridge.

Literature of earlier years, particularly for the purpose of describing the few British examples of alternative silvicultural systems, indicated some confusion in their classification. Professor Matthews's admirable text (1989) effected clarification, and with his permission and that of Clarendon Press, Oxford his classification and descriptions of systems have been followed. The courtesy and assistance thus extended has enabled this Bulletin to benefit from a sound base on which to record past and present and suggest potential relevant practices in Britain. Nonetheless, readers will benefit by study of Professor Matthews's text as well as those of Evans (1988) and Kerr and Evans (1993).

Information gained by membership of the Continuous Cover Forestry Group, inaugurated in 1991, and from the Edinburgh University database on examples of irregular silvicultural systems in Britain is warmly acknowledged. Profound thanks are recorded to the owners and/or their foresters of many private sector woodland stands visited; also to managers of Forest

Enterprise's relevant forest stands, where my visits have been welcomed and proved rewarding to me. I not only ended up with many friends but with a very large number of obligations.

This Bulletin is written for landowners and foresters who wish to convert all or part of a wood or forest from pure, regular, uniform, even-aged stands to mixed, irregular, uneven-aged stands – in particular for those who desire to use silvicultural systems alternative to that of extensive clear cutting, with a view to achieving diverse structure leading to biological diversity and semi-permanent or continuous forest cover. The information provided can be adopted to suit individual owners' or foresters' own constraints and objectives. Other aims are to draw attention to what has been achieved in Britain, and the opportunities for further attempts, and to highlight the need for further research, trials and demonstration areas.

A few of the plates were taken by myself; others were taken by my son, Anthony, and by friends in the forestry world; the remainder were selected from the Forestry Commission's photographic library. Permission of John Matthews CBE (Emeritus Professor, University of Aberdeen), David Paterson and Chris Quine to include certain tables (amended) is gratefully acknowledged: the sources are recorded in appropriate places in the text.

Cyril Hart
1995

Foreword

Compared with much of Europe, British forestry has largely been dominated by just one silvicultural system in recent decades, viz. clearfelling and replanting. There are sound silvicultural reasons for this, in particular the windiness of our upland climate. Nevertheless, today, there is increasing interest in extending rotation lengths and in diversifying forest structure which, along with greater attention to lowland woods, create more opportunities for alternative silvicultural systems. This Bulletin draws together experience in Britain with many different types of silviculture which have been tried out or practised during the present century. I hope foresters, woodland owners, and all those interested in the management of Britain's woodlands and forests will find the assemblage of experience of considerable use.

The Forestry Commission is deeply indebted to Dr Cyril Hart OBE for bringing together, analysing and synthesising experience with these alternative silvicultural systems from all parts of the country. This task has not been easy and the Forestry Commission is most grateful that the job has been undertaken by one so eminent.

I hope that readers will find the text itself informative and interesting and the plates instructive of the different kinds of silviculture discussed. Each detailed account of individual woods and the silvicultural system practised is headlined in colour. It is these descriptions, brought together for the first time, which are at the heart of this Bulletin and, I believe, will make it such an invaluable reference work in the future.

T.R. Cutler CBE
Director General
Forestry Commission
June 1995

WITHDRAWN

Contents

		Page
Acknowledgements		iii
Foreword		v
List of plates		viii
Summary		x
Résumé		xi
Zusammenfassung		xiii
Resumen		xiv
1 Diverse woods and forests: the role of silvicultural systems		1
Introduction		1
Alternative silvicultural systems to clear cutting		2
Preparatory work in conversion		5
2 Shelterwood systems		6
Introduction		6
Use in Britain: broadleaves		8
Uniform shelterwood		8
Group shelterwood		10
Use in Britain: conifers		12
Uniform and group shelterwood		12
Conclusions on shelterwood systems		14
3 The group selection system		17
Introduction		17
Use in Britain: broadleaves		17
Use in Britain: conifers and mixed stands		25
Conclusions on the group selection system		35
4 The single tree selection system		39
Introduction		39
Application on the Continent		39
Use in Britain		41
Conclusions on the single tree selection system		44
5 Other silvicultural systems		46
Two-storied high forest		46
High forest with reserves		48
Coppice and coppice with standards		49
Restructuring extensive conifer forest by patch clear cutting		50

Restructuring beechwoods by (mainly) group regeneration 52
Conclusions on other silvicultural systems 53

6 The economics of irregular forestry 54
Introduction 54
The single tree selection system 55
The shelterwood uniform and group systems 56
The economic justification of uneven-aged and continuous forest cover 56
Conclusions on the economics of irregular forestry 57

7 Influence of environmental factors on alternative silvicultural systems and conversion 58
Effect of wind 58
Effect of damaging mammals 60
   Deer 60
   Grey squirrels 61
Effects on landscape 61
Impact on nature conservation 62
Effect on recreational potential 63
Conclusions on the influence of environmental factors 63

8 Conclusions: resources and benefits, opportunities and recommendations 64
General 64
Experience in Britain 65
Opportunities in Britain 65
Conversion 68
Summary of benefits of alternative systems 69
   Environmental benefits 69
   Silvicultural benefits 69
Management economics of alternative systems 70
Postscript 71

References 72

Glossary 1 Definition of terms 78
Glossary 2 Scientific names and authorities of the main English
   names used in the text 80

Appendix 1 Classification of silvicultural systems 81
Appendix 2 Summary of factors to consider in choosing silvicultural
   systems 82
Appendix 3 Need for research, trials and demonstration areas 84
Appendix 4 Suggestions for trials and demonstration areas 88
Appendix 5 History and personalities 89

List of plates

1 Natural regeneration of oak and beech at Churchill East, Forest of Dean

2 Beech natural regeneration at Savernake Forest, Wiltshire, showing older groups becoming diverse in canopy structure and age

3 Pedunculate oak natural regeneration at High Standing Hill Wood, Windsor Forest

4 Natural regeneration of oak, improved by fencing to exclude mammals, at Wyre Forest

5 Douglas fir and Norway spruce group shelterwood system at The Hermitage Wood, near Dunkeld

6 Natural regeneration of grand fir in a uniform shelterwood system at High Standing Hill Wood, Windsor Forest

7 Scots pine natural regeneration under a uniform shelterwood system at the Crown Estate, Swinley

8 Beech natural regeneration under 110-year-old trees at Workmans Wood, Ebworth, Gloucestershire

9 European larch at Cawdor Big Wood, near Nairn

10 Oak trees in fog at Cawdor Big Wood, near Nairn

11 The Glentress Trial, Glentress Forest, near Peebles: conversion of conifer stands from uniform even-aged clear cutting system to uneven-aged group selection

12 Conversion of conifers to group selection system at Corrour Forest, Inverness-shire

13 Old Scots pine at Faskally Wood, near Pitlochry, showing conversion towards group selection in conifers

14 Group or random regeneration of indigenous Scots pine at Benevean Wood, Glen Affric

15 Douglas fir at Diosgydd, Gwynedd, illustrating conversion of conifer plantations to group selection

16 Sitka spruce and beech natural regeneration under mature larch at Nant BH, Gwynedd

17 Shelterwood-cum-group selection system at Longleat, Wiltshire, showing natural regeneration under Douglas fir

18 Prolific natural regeneration of Western hemlock in a single tree selection system at Kyloe Wood, Northumberland

19 Kielder Forest: restructuring for increasingly multiple purpose objectives

20 Hamsterley Forest: smaller scale restructuring

21 Group regeneration of beech in the Chilterns

22 A mixed storey formed by regenerating beech in the Chilterns

23 Restructuring of beechwoods in the Chilterns by group regeneration
    under a stand of *c*. 150-year-old beech

24 Professor Mark Loudon Anderson

Alternative Silvicultural Systems to Clear Cutting in Britain: A Review

Summary

The objective of this Bulletin is to summarise British experience of alternative silvicultural systems to clear cutting. Management of woodlands for diverse objectives such as recreation, landscape, timber production and conservation is becoming increasingly important. Irregular forestry systems have been promoted as one way of maximising the potential benefits woodlands have to offer. This Bulletin explores this assumption and highlights the lessons which have been learnt in managing irregular forestry, and in converting high forest managed by clear cutting to other systems.

The examples described have been classified into: shelterwood, group selection, single tree selection and other silvicultural systems. In total 44 examples of managing forest areas using alternative silvicultural systems, in upland and lowland Britain, are described; these include the well-known examples of Glentress, Ebworth, Weasenham and Dartington. Brief consideration is also given to the economics of irregular forestry and the effects of environmental factors on transformation to alternative silvicultural systems.

The Bulletin emphasises four key considerations influencing the use of irregular forestry:

1. The use of irregular silvicultural systems is possible on a wide range of sites in upland and lowland Britain.

2. The key to success for irregular forestry in Britain is continuity of management. The forester must possess a sound knowledge of silviculture, have an intimate acquaintance with the stands in question, and be prepared to be innovative, patient and opportunistic in the application of, or conversion to, the chosen silvicultural system.

3. The costs of management of irregular forestry can be high compared with the clear cutting system, hence it is not favoured by conventional economic analysis based on financial yield. Such analyses invariably favour systems of low management cost.

4. The potential of irregular forestry to produce non-market benefits can be high compared with the clear cutting system. More research into the evaluation of such benefits is required so that irregular forestry can be compared objectively with other silvicultural systems.

The Bulletin concludes that there are many opportunities to pursue irregular forestry practices more widely throughout Britain.

Régimes de sylviculture utilisés en alternative à la coupe rase en Grande-Bretagne: une revue

Résumé

L'objectif de ce bulletin est de résumer l'expérience effectuée en Grande-Bretagne sur les régimes de sylviculture offrant une alternative à la coupe rase. La gestion des bois à des fins diverses telles que la détente, le paysage, la production de bois et la conservation devient de plus en plus importante. Les régimes de foresterie irrégulière ont été encouragés en tant que moyen de maximiser les avantages que les bois ont le potentiel d'offrir. Ce bulletin étudie cette hypothèse et met en relief les enseignements tirés de la gestion de la sylviculture irrégulière et de la conversion à d'autres régimes des hautes futaies précédemment gérées à l'aide de la coupe rase.

Les examples décrits ont été classés de la manière suivante: abri (coupes progressives), jardinage par bouquets, jardinage et autres régimes de sylviculture. Au total, 44 exemples de gestion de la forêt à l'aide de régimes de sylviculture utilisés comme alternative dans les hautes et basses terres de Grande-Bretagne se trouvent décrits. Parmi ceux-ci figurent les exemples bien connus de Glentress, Ebworth, Weasenham et Dartington. La rentabilité de la foresterie irrégulière est aussi brièvement abordée de même que les effets qu'ont les facteurs écologiques sur la transformation en faveur des régimes de sylviculture utilisés comme alternative.

Le bulletin met l'accent sur quatre considérations clés influençant le recours à la foresterie irrégulière:

1. L'utilisation de régimes de sylviculture irrégulière est possible dans une grande variété de sites se trouvant dans les hautes et basses terres de Grande-Bretagne.

2. La clé du succès en matière de foresterie irrégulière en Grande-Bretagne se trouve dans la continuité de la gestion. Quand il s'agit d'opérer la conversion au régime de sylviculture choisi ou d'appliquer ce dernier, le forestier doit posséder une bonne connaissance de la sylviculture, être très au courant des positions en question et être prêt à innover, à se montrer patient et à saisir les occasions se présentant.

3. Les coûts de gestion de la foresterie irrégulière peuvent être élevés par comparaison à ceux du régime utilisant la coupe rase. De ce fait, l'analyse économique conventionnelle basée sur le rendement financier ne lui est pas favorable. De telles analyses favorisent invariablement les systèmes ayant des coûts de gestion peu élevés.

4. Le potentiel montré par la foresterie irrégulière lorsqu'il s'agit de produire des bénéfices n'ayant rien à voir avec le marché peut être élevé par com-

paraison avec le régime utilisant la coupe rasc. Il s'avère nécessaire de procéder à une évaluation plus approfondie de tels bénéfices afin de comparer objectivement la foresterie irrégulière aux autres régimes de sylviculture.

Le Bulletin conclut qu'il existe de nombreuses occasions d'accroître la mise en pratique de la foresterie irrégulière dans toute la Grande-Bretagne.

Forstwirtschaftliche Alternativen zum Kahlschlag in Britannien: Eine Übersicht

Zusammenfassung

Der Zweck dieses Bulletins ist die Darlegung de britischen Erfahrungen mit forstwirtschaftlichen Alternativen zum Kahlschlag. Es wird immer wichtiger, Forstwirtschaft so zu betreiben, daß diverse Ziele wie etwa Erhohlung, Landschaftsgestaltung, Holzproduktion und Naturschutz erreicht werden können. Unregelmäßige Forstwirtschaftssysteme werden als eine Art zur Maximierung der möglichen Nutzen, die Wälder bitten, vorgeschlagen. Diese Bulletin untersucht diese Ansicht und hebt die Erfahrungen hervor, die durch unregelmäßige Forstwirtschaft und die Umstellung von Hochwaldbewirtschaftung durch Kahlschlag auf andere Systeme, gewonnen wurden.

Die Beispiele die hier beschrieben werden, sind wie folgt unterteilt: Schutzwald, Gruppenauswahl, Einzelbaumauswahl oder andere Systeme. Insgesamt 44 Hoch- und Niederland - Forstgebiete, beschrieben die nach alternativen Systemen bewirtschaftet werden. Darunter sind unter anderem die bekannten Beispiele von Glentress, Ebworth, Weasenham und Dartington. Die Wirtschaftlichkeit unregelmäßiger Forstwirtschaft wird kurz behandelt, sowie die Wirkung von Umweltfaktoren auf die Umstellung auf alternative Systeme.

Dieses Bulletin unterstreicht die vier Hauptfaktoren, die den Gebrauch von unregelmäßiger Forstwirtschaft beeinflussen:

1. Der Gebrauch von unregelmäßigen Forstwirtschaftssystemen ist bei einer großen Anzahl von Standorten im Hoch- und Niederland Britanniens möglich.

2. Der Schlüssel zum Erfolg von unregelmäßiger Forstwirtschaft liegt in der Stetigkeit der Pflege. Der Förster muß ein gutes Kenntnis der Forstkultur haben, die betroffenen Stände genau kennen und bereit sein, innovativ, geduldig und opportunistisch in der Anwendung, oder Umstellung, des gewählten forstwirtschaftlichen Systems, vorzugehen.

3. Die Kosten der unregelmäßigen Forstwirtschaft können, im Vergleich zu Kahlschlag, hoch sein, dadurch wird es bei normaler finanzieller Analyse der Erträge nicht vorgezogen. Solche Analysen ziehen unweigerlich Systeme mit niedrigen Pflegekosten vor.

4. Unregelmäßige Forstwirtschaft kann, im Vergleich zum Kahlschlagsystem, ein großes Potential an nichtwirtschaftlichen Nutzen bieten. Es sind mehr Untersuchungen in die Bewertung dieser anderen Nutzen nötig, so daß unregelmäßige Forstwirtschaft objektiv mit anderen Systemen verglichen werden kann.

Dieses Bulletin zieht den Schluß, daß es viele Gelegenheiten gibt, unregelmäßige Forstwirtschaft in größerem Umfang zu benutzen überall Großbrittanien.

Sistemas Silviculturales Como Alternatives a la Corta a Hecho en Gran Bretaña: Una Revista

Resumen

Este Boletín tiene por objeto resumir la experiencia británica con sistemas silviculturales como alternativas a la corta a hecho. La ordenación de bosques para objetos diversos como recreo, paisaje, producción maderable, y conservación llega a ser cada vez más importante. Se fomentan sistemas forestales irregulares como un método de maximar los beneficios potenciales que ofrecen los bosques. Este Boletín trata de esta suposición, y destaca las conclusiones, aprendidas en la ordenación de dasonomía irregular, y en la conversión de un regimen en monte alto con corta a hecho a otros sistemas.

Se clasifican los ejemplos descritos como sigue: cortas por aclareos sucesivos; entresaca por bosquetes; selección (entresaca) individual; y otros sistemas silviculturales. En suma, se describe 44 ejemplos del tratamiento de bosques por sistemas silviculturales alternativos, en las tierras altas y en las tierras bajas de Gran Bretaña; estos ejemplos incluyen los bosques conocidos de Glentress, Ebworth, Weasenham y Dartington. Se tratan brevemente también los aspectos económicos de dasonomía irregular, y los efectos de factores environmentales sobre la transformación en sistemas silviculturales alternativos.

Este Boletín hace resaltar cuatro consideraciones principales que afectan el uso de dasonomía irregular:

1. El uso de sistemas silviculturales irregulares es posible en una gama ancha de sitios en las tierras altas y bajas en Gran Bretaña.

2. La llave al éxito para la dasonomía irregular en Gran Bretaña es la continuidad del tratamiento. El ingeniero forestal debe ser experto en la silvicultura, debe conocer íntimamente las masas particulares, y debe ser innovador, paciente y oportunista en la aplicación del sistema silvicultural elegido, o en la conversión del sistema.

3. Los costes de la ordenación de dasonomía irregular pueden ser altos en comparación con la corta a hecho, y por esto no se favorece por un análisis económico convencional a base del rendimiento en dinero. Tales análises siempre favorecen los sistemas con costes bajos de ordenación.

4. El potencial de dasonomía irregular para producir beneficios no-mercados puede ser alto en comparación con el sistema corta a hecho. Se necesita más investigaciones en la valuación de tales beneficios, para hacer una comparación objetiva de la dasonomía irregular con otros sistemas silviculturales.

Este Boletín concluye que hay muchas oportunidades para practicar tratamientos silviculturales irregulares en escala más grande a través de todo la Gran Bretaña.

Chapter 1

Diverse woods and forests: the role of silvicultural systems

Introduction

In Europe many silvicultural systems have been used for centuries; and in recent years the organisation Pro Silva has given increased attention to extension of uneven-aged, irregular systems including 'continuous cover forest' and so-called 'near to nature forestry'. In Britain, during this century, most silviculture has been under the extensive clear cutting system, supplemented by the coppice and coppice with standards systems. However, in recent decades, the clear cutting system, despite its many valuable attributes, has received some disapproval because of sudden changes on landscape, amenity, wildlife conservation and recreation. Continuous forest cover and 'naturalness' are increasingly thought of as desirable for multi-purpose objectives where locations, sites and conditions are suitable.

These changes are reflected in the present policy of Government on woods and forests in Britain which emphasises that foresters should integrate the production of timber with the desired aesthetic, recreational and environmental benefits; also that they should recognise their protective functions in relation to soil, water and air quality, and manage to protect and enhance them. Part of the process of meeting these requirements is to accelerate the diversity of young woods and forests and develop their structure to achieve harmony with the landscape and gain environmental benefits.

All these topics fall within the province of silvicultural systems which result in the production of stands of distinctive form; and the individual stands together make up whole woods and forests of distinctive form. Silvicultural systems are ecological means of achieving management objectives. They specify the method of regenerating new stands, the form of stand produced, and their spatial arrangement over the forest. This planned arrangement takes care of an essential group of requirements, namely the efficient harvesting of the produce, the protection of the wood or forest against damage by wind, fire and animals, and reaction to attacks of insect pests and diseases. Where a forest is part of a water catchment, the arrangement of stands can sometimes be used to assist in regulating water supplies.

In the great majority of older woods and forests in Britain timber production has been and remains of prime importance but experience has shown that the sustained yield of timber can be integrated with aesthetic, recreational and environmental benefits when a range of age classes and size classes exist. This is because, in the traditional clear cutting and restocking silvicultural system, each stage of development of a stand has certain distinct characters. When the trees are young, there is plenty of open space and abundant habitat and food for birds and animals. But when the trees form canopy and enter the thicket stage they dominate the site and suppress or exclude ground flora and restrict the diversity of wildlife. Then, as the trees gain in stature, the structure of the stand becomes more open; as the live crowns move up above the ground and the processes of thinning and harvesting trees marked for removal admit light, the habitat is improved for a greater variety of wildlife on the ground, in the crowns and around the edges. The ideal for recreational and environmental benefits is to create open space in and around the stands of trees, and to arrange newly regenerated stands close to those approaching maturity. These benefits follow from forests that are close to the stage of sustained yield of timber; in other words, the forests have a balanced growing stock that can produce timber as well as the other benefits already mentioned, in perpetuity.

A medium sized wood or small forest of (say) 150 to 360 hectares (ha) in extent, managed on the more recently introduced patch clear cutting system (see Chapter 5) with a rotation of 50 to 60 years, may comprise 50 to 60 stands, each of 3 to 6 ha. If the boundaries of individual stands or of groups of stands have been designed to fit the landscape, the edges of extraction routes and other open spaces are treated to favour broadleaved trees, shrubs and interesting ground flora, and young stands adjoin older ones, there will be considerable diversity in appearance, structure and habitat. If two or more species are used, the diversity will increase further. In larger forests, use of the clear cutting system will give the impression of less variety, but this does not mean that diversity is absent: it is just more dispersed and on a larger scale. This is a problem particularly of large forests in the uplands, and examples of restructuring and alternative silvicultural systems for the uplands are described in Chapters 2-5.

Lucas (1991) states that diversity is 'the degree and number of differences in a composition'; and that 'an important principle of design is to achieve sufficient diversity to create interest without causing loss of unity'. The components of diversity in forestry include species composition, canopy structure, size and shape of stands, the use of open space (roads, streams, pools and glades), the spatial arrangement of individual stands, and the provision of habitat for wildlife. However, a diverse structure is not permanent: it is in fact very dynamic with shifting time components of stands as they age, develop, mature and are regenerated on a small scale. Forest cover is the permanence. In practice, some of these components are classified as follows:

1. Stands are classed *pure* when they consist of one principal species, and *mixed* when there are more than one.

2. A stand with only one canopy of foliage is *uniform*. If there are two distinct canopies, the term used is *two-storied high forest,* but this structure is not permanent, although it often persists for an appreciable time. *Coppice with standards* has an overwood of mixed ages and an even-aged underwood of coppice; this is permanent provided there is periodic recruitment to the standards and the coppice is not stored. If there are more than two canopies of foliage, the term used is *selection forest* or sometimes *continuous canopy forest* (although the latter is a general description and not a definition).

3. When the ages of the trees in a stand are within a few years of each other, the term used is *regular* or *even-aged;* when the ages differ by more than 15 to 20 years, the stand is *irregular* or *uneven-aged.*

A classification of silvicultural systems (following Matthews, 1989) is given in Appendix 1. A brief history of attempts at alternative systems to clear cutting in Britain, and an introduction to some of the earlier practitioners, are given in Appendix 5.

Alternative silvicultural systems to clear cutting

Several alternative silvicultural systems can be used in suitable locations in place of clear cutting, and these are distinguished by the length of the period of regeneration, the proportion of the previous stand that is retained as seedbearers or upper canopy, and the preferred scale of operations. Because of the familiarity of clear cutting, it will be convenient to make comparisons with it to provide a reference point.

In the *clear cutting* system all the old stand is felled in one operation. The new stand is regenerated, usually by planting but sometimes naturally, and generally establishes itself without any shelter from the old canopy. This simple procedure is acceptable for species that are hardy and demand full light to grow, e.g. larches, pines, birches and oaks, and it is a reliable way of restocking with pure or mixed species of light-demanders. It provides an opportunity to introduce new cultivars with improved performance. The range in scale of operations is varied but, when the individual coupes decline in area to about 2 ha, the benefits of scale tend to be lost and the system gives way to others.

When a forester wishes to use the old stand to provide seed and shelter for the regeneration and early development of a new crop, a group of silvicultural systems called the *shelterwood systems* (see Chapter 2) can be used. The old stand is felled in two or three stages during 10 to 30 years depending on circumstances. The new crop regenerates and becomes established under the changing conditions produced by manipulating the retained seedbearers in the old stand. The amount of shelter produced by overhead shading and/or side shading can be used to stimulate the formation of mixed stands. The systems commonly include the use of planting to reinforce the stocking from natural regeneration, or to adjust the species mixture. Species which are initially frost tender and prefer shade during regeneration are favoured in the longer regeneration periods, e.g. beech, Douglas fir, grand fir, western hemlock. Shorter regeneration periods and more uniform regeneration occur with oak, ash and sycamore.

The phased removal of the old stand may be effected over quite large areas, the *uniform shelterwood system*, or may start from several small nuclei which are gradually extended and eventually merge, the *group shelterwoood system*. Alternatively, when it is done in strips, or in groups organised into strips the *shelterwood strip system* and *strip and group system* are being used. If adequate seed production occurs at short intervals or prompt recourse is made to enrichment planting, the new crop is quickly established, and is even-aged and regular in appearance like that in the clear cutting system. But seed production can be spasmodic and less abundant, so several seed years may be needed and eventually planting done to fill the gappy regeneration; in the latter case the new stand tends to be irregular in age and size; but after cleanings and early thinnings the stand becomes more regular in appearance.

In all shelterwood systems the two stands, one mature and the other young, grow on the same site for several years. In the pines, the regeneration period is normally up to 10 to 15 years; in oak and beech and mixtures of these two species, the time taken to remove the old trees is usually 20 to 30 years but can be shorter if good regeneration is obtained early. During the regeneration period the stand is two-storied and may consist of two or more species. The diversity in appearance and habitat can be rich; moreover, in some cases some of the best seedbearers may be retained as standards and the dense lower canopy gradually ascends to meet the sparse upper one.

When one of the shelterwood systems is applied to coupes of (say) 10 to 25 ha, seed production is regular, and good prices are obtained for large, high quality logs, the time and attention to detail demanded from the forester is repaid. Great emphasis is placed on the ground conditions so that weed growth does not inhibit the germination and growth of natural regeneration; and the stands are carefully thinned so that the seedbearers can be selected from among windfirm trees with stems of high quality. A high managerial input is ultimately rewarded by good financial returns. But in Britain there are few places where large stands of quality broadleaves exist that will repay adoption of the shelterwood systems; a notable exception is part of the Forest of Dean. The systems can be widely applied to light-demanding conifers provided that the windthrow hazard classification of the site does not exceed 3 (or perhaps 4 with stand preparation) and the soil is freely drained. Examples given in Chapter 2 will allow readers to judge for themselves.

Some silvicultural systems can create similar diversity in species, structure, appearance and habitat in *all parts of the forest*. Instead of large open spaces at regeneration time, as are required by the extensive clear cutting and shelterwood systems, the forester manipulates a continuous canopy, which is only partially broken when regeneration is to be favoured, and then over quite small areas. The forester seeks to create a 'natural' appearance which is sustained for as long as possible, and ideally in perpetuity.

When the regeneration period is lengthened, the stand becomes more varied in age and size, and more irregular in structure. If it takes half the rotation to restock part of a forest, that part will contain trees ranging in age from (say) 1 to 50 years. If the regeneration period is equal to the time taken to reach an exploitable diameter, the whole forest is being regenerated continually and becomes completely irregular in structure. In practice, the whole management plan area is usually divided into parts or blocks and the work of felling mature trees, making thinnings and cleanings and favouring new regeneration is done in different parts, usually on a 6-year cycle. The first situation described above leads to the *irregular shelterwood system*, and the second to the two *selection systems* (see Chapters 3 and 4). If the sites being regenerated are each roughly equal to the crown spread of one or two mature trees, the system is *single tree selection* (see Chapter 4); and if each area cleared is made larger so as to allow for light-demanding and moderate shade-bearing species the system is *group selection* (see Chapter 3).

The ideal condition of a forest produced by the *irregular shelterwood system* is a varied canopy of groups of the favoured species, retention of mature and maturing stands so long as they fulfil their function, whether of sustained production of timber, or maintaining site conditions, filling gaps in a range of age classes and size classes or providing diversity. There is no formal statement of rotation. The system is often used in Europe to introduce a shade-bearing mixture of beech and European silver fir into stands of pure, even-aged Norway spruce. The result is often a forest of fine appearance, which because of the emphasis placed on improving the site conditions and the quality of the growing stock is also productive in both yield and income. However, the conventional irregular shelterwood system (Femelschlag in German) has so far been untested in Britain, and only small scale variants of it are mentioned in this Bulletin.

The conditions of *single tree selection* forest (see Chapter 4) can be appreciated by imagining being in a place surrounded by trees ranging from the smallest to the largest in the forest. The young trees are rather slowly grown but are of shade-tolerant species able to recover when they receive adequate light. The canopy is complete and very deep, extending right down to ground level; there are usually three canopy layers which approximate to small-sized, middle-sized and large trees (classes often used in enumerations). The most obvious size classes in the mixture are the middle and large trees and it is among these that thinnings are undertaken to adjust the distribution of size classes, which in theory must correspond in numbers to a stem-number curve for the stand type. The stems of large trees in the upper canopy are usually strongly tapered, but of a good size and well suited to the market. The species will vary, but in Switzerland and other parts of central Europe a mixture of Norway spruce, European silver fir and beech is commonly found. In Britain, European silver fir is usually attacked by *Adelges nusslini* and is not widely planted; however, it can be replaced by some useful exotics such as noble, grand, Caucasian and Pacific firs, and western red cedar and western hemlock. Sycamore and Norway maple may supplement beech.

The *group selection* system (see Chapter 3) seems to be well suited to the small scale of much forestry in the lowlands of Britain. Here a great deal of the broadleaved silviculture depends on light-demanding species including ash and wild cherry (gean) but the system is also relevant, using smaller groups, to beech, sycamore and Norway maple. A wood or forest managed by the group selection system reveals a series of groups originating at different times, up to 0.6 and even 1.0 ha in size, growing side by side and in various stages of treatment, e.g. cleaning, thinning, and others restocked after felling. This diversity over small distances is made possible by the small size of the groups which are encouraged to blend together to exploit the mutual synergy between species.

Not all the benefits claimed for mixed, uneven-aged forests produced by the two selection systems can be completely substantiated. Such forests are said to be resistant to fire, but most are used in areas where fires are infrequent. They are also claimed to be more resistant to wind and snow and to be more flexible to meet storm or pest events than forests produced by clear cutting and shelterwood systems, a claim that seems to be borne out in practice. The argument that uneven-aged systems produce similar or even greater yields than regular forests can be resolved rather simply as follows: if the ground in the cases being compared is covered by a complete canopy of foliage of the same species, why should there not be roughly equal production of dry matter or timber? If both stands are fully stocked, there should be similar yields; in practice, however, it is easier to control stocking in an even-aged stand than in an uneven-aged one, but the structure in the former can be more vulnerable to storm events.

One great advantage of *selection* forest is that good quality trees can be retained for as long as they are producing an acceptable increment, and this leads to a potent argument that is easy to accept, namely that the financial yield of irregular forest is at least equal to that of comparable regular forest. It is also possible to resolve in similar unsophisticated terms the argument that the costs of management of irregular forest are high. The counter-argument runs as follows: given that the silvicultural costs and those of management are higher than those of comparable regular forest, the costs could match the benefits if a value was placed on *permanent* amenity, recreation and the provision of habitat for wildlife. Irregular forest and the selection systems are clearly the better providers of these benefits.

Preparatory work in conversion

The particular features of diversity being sought will normally be obtained by taking an area of woodland or forest and converting (or transforming) it to an alternative silvicultural system. British foresters are normally not familiar with converting plantations into forests because so many of our stands are pure, even-aged and regular, and clear cutting has been the system adopted previously. The object is to make some of the area mixed, uneven-aged and irregular by lengthening the regeneration period, breaking up the existing structure, and using systems other than extensive clear cutting. The process must begin *early* and at not later than 40 years in conifer stands and 60 to 80 years in broadleaved stands.

Remaining after the selection felling of broadleaves during World War II (1939-1945) was a jumble of 'derelict woodland' (see Chapter 3). Some of this area was converted by clearing and replanting, enrichment, or underplanting, together with cleaning and thinning of well-stocked and promising groups of advanced natural growth and older stands. The success of these operations during the post-war years provided good examples for foresters in how to deal with degraded broadleaved stands by adapting these silvicultural techniques and using alternative systems of silviculture to create new forms of stands, woods and forests. Thus, if there are existing woods which contain small groups of regeneration with some straight, vigorous and well-formed trees, or larger stands either pure or with a mixture of species, or old trees that will survive for some years, these can form a basis for conversion to a new system. Old poor quality trees or groups can be felled to form new regeneration groups. Glades can either be planted or left unstocked as part of the conservation management plan. The details of operations done to make conversion from one form of such woodland to another are described by Garfitt (1980, 1984), Evans (1984), Matthews (1989) and Hart (1991), and are further discussed in this Bulletin.

The attempts at uneven-aged forestry in Britain have been made by foresters who have been enthusiastic and patient, also opportunistic and flexible in management, not always adhering to any formal system, so that it is difficult to classify some of the examples in this Bulletin because distinctions between variants and adaptations have become blurred.

Chapter 2
Shelterwood systems

Introduction

Shelterwood systems have many variants but essentially involve partially felling a stand to leave a scattered overstorey of mature trees (as seedbearers); regeneration then takes place in the overhead or side shelter of the seedbearing trees. Planting is used only to supplement areas where natural regeneration is inadequate or has failed. In Britain the systems have been used for conifers, particularly Scots pine, but less used for broadleaves; however, under the right conditions they have succeeded, and are particularly suitable for heavy seeded species such as oak and beech (Table 2.1), although the shade regime has to be handled carefully for the latter (Evans, 1984, 1988; Kerr and Evans, 1993). The traditional method comprises seeding, secondary and final fellings, which are described in detail by Matthews (1989). Its use for conifers is most common in regions with warm summers favouring seed production, on sites with low windthrow hazard (WHC 1-3), deep soils, light weed growth and flat to moderate terrain. The systems' main advantages are that they produce uniform pure or mixed crops over large areas; and the seedbearers add valuable increment to compensate for any longer regeneration periods. Their main disadvantage is that a long period of preparation is required to make dominants into windfirm seedbearers.

- *Uniform shelterwood system* In the uniform shelterwood system the whole stand is opened up uniformly for regeneration purposes, and promotes a largely uniform and even-aged young crop. To systematise operations and ensure that the whole management unit shall be felled and regenerated during the course of a rotation, the traditional approach is to divide a forest into a number of 'periodic blocks', each to be felled and regenerated in turn during the course of successive 'periods' (Matthews, 1989; Benezit, 1991). The system practised on the Continent with oak and beech has been discussed by Everard (1985), and with Scots pine, larch, European silver fir or Norway spruce by Yorke (1991a, b).

- *Group shelterwood system* Group shelterwood is similar to uniform shelterwood but regeneration is in groups, usually under 0.6 ha. It involves the opening up of the canopy by scattered groups which may need preparation by thinning of the margins.

- *Shelterwood strip systems* The shelterwood strip systems include *strip and group*, and *wedge*. They are devised for regions with more windy climates, on sites with brown earths, podzols, and occasionally gleyed soils, and on flat, moderate or occasionally steep terrain. Foresters can use the systems in mixtures containing light-demanders (pine or larch), moderate shade-bearers (spruces or sycamore) and shade-bearers (beech or silver firs). The main advantages are that they provide sheltered regeneration sites and control of the micro-climate through use of overhead and side shade. Skilled directional felling is involved but harvesting is easy to organise. When used in progressive fashion, the systems can be visually attractive. The main disadvantage is the requirement for careful thinning to create stable edges on the inner and outer strips. The wedge system can be used on

Table 2.1. The location of stands treated by the uniform and group shelterwood systems

	Ownership	Wind zone [a]	Main shelterwood system	Main species
England				
Forest of Dean	Forest Enterprise	3	Uniform-Group	Pedunculate oak
Savernake Forest	Forest Enterprise (lease)	1	Group	Beech
Slindon Park, West Sussex - terminated	National Trust	2–3	Uniform	Beech
Windsor Forest				
Cranbourne Wood	Crown Estates	2	Uniform	Pedunculate oak
High Standing Hill Wood	Crown Estates	2	Uniform	Pedunculate oak
Wakefield Estate (Northants)	Private	3	Uniform	Ash
Wyre Forest	English Nature	3	Group	Sessile oak
Wyre Forest	Forest Enterprise	3	Uniform	Douglas fir
Watlington Forest Queen Wood	Forest Enterprise	1	Group	Beech
Windsor Forest				
High Standing Hill Wood	Crown Estates	2	Uniform	Grand fir
Swinley	Crown Estates	2	Uniform	Scots pine
Scotland				
Glen Tanar Estate Aboyne	Michael Bruce	5	Uniform	Scots pine
Craigvinean Forest, Dunkeld	Forest Enterprise	3	Group	Douglas fir
The Hermitage Wood, Dunkeld	National Trust for Scotland	3	Group	Douglas fir
Grampian and Tayside	Forest Enterprise	3-5	Underplant	Firs etc.

[a] Wind zone describes the regional windiness for the site; values obtained from Quine and White (1993) and Quine (personal communications for areas in SE England). See Glossary 1 for further definition.

sites with moderate windthrow hazard (WHC 3-4) provided the soils are quite deep; in Britain it is worth testing on gleyed soils with Sitka and Norway spruces in moist (not wet) regions.

Use in Britain : broadleaves

Uniform shelterwood

The uniform shelterwood system has been little used on broadleaves in Britain. Few British foresters have gained the experience and skill needed to promote and manage natural regeneration. Other factors which make the system less easy to apply to oak and beech in Britain are high densities of deer and rabbits, and predation from pigeons and mice is also very high. In addition, an important difference between Britain and the Continent is the lower frequency of good mast years; also absence of ground 'cultivation' by wild boar. Troup (1952) and Evans (1988) listed good mast years for beech in Britain in the first half of this century, and emphasised that they are not only less frequent but also more erratic in occurrence than on the Continent. Foresters can do little to increase this supply of seed apart from increasing the size and vigour of crowns of seedbearers by crown thinning (Matthews, 1963; Evans, 1988). But, apart from this difference in seed supply, there are no obvious ecological differences between Continental and British conditions, although shade is better used to keep a clear forest floor in Europe. Selective felling and lack of understorey have often allowed the forest floor to receive too much light and to become invaded by grasses and bramble. Several foresters have attempted to use the uniform shelterwood system for broadleaves in Britain. Five notable examples are described.

Forest of Dean, Gloucestershire

At Blakeney Hill West, after seeding fellings, excellent regeneration of pedunculate oak resulted from an abundance of mast in 1899, protected with fencing against sheep (Troup, 1928, 1952; Hart, 1966, 1991). Some 160 ha were established in this way. At Sutton Bottom, 11 ha were regenerated in 1909. A gradual removal of the overstorey oak was made. Gaps were planted with Norway spruce, sycamore and European larch. Fine stands of oak resulted and these were underplanted with beech by 1952. The stands are referred to as 'Hanson's oak'.

At Churchill East (Plate 1), the uniform shelterwood system is being used to regenerate a 1857 stand of pedunculate oak and beech on shallow brown earth over broken rock. Following a heavy oak mast in 1989, the broadleaved understorey on 3.5 ha was removed in 1990, and a seeding regeneration felling of the overwood left a 60% canopy. A secondary felling followed in 1991. In each felling the hardwood lop and top was placed around the base of the remaining parent trees so as not to hinder weeding of the young crop. The natural regeneration of oak at present is 10-40 cm tall and equalled by a similar amount of beech, though slight damage has been done by caterpillars and oak mildew. The young plants are lightly top-weeded, mainly in bracken. A further secondary felling was planned for 1993. The final felling, with the exception of 5-10 large oak reserves per hectare, will be done in 3-5 years time. The eventual aim for the new stand is a 50/50 mix of oak and beech, most of the latter to be managed as an understorey for the benefit of the oak (J. Everard, personal communication).

Savernake Forest, Wiltshire

This former ancient royal forest is now privately owned but was leased to the Forestry Commission from 1939. For several centuries it appears to have been used mainly as woodland pasture with small copses and woods within. Old beech from the 1740s indicate that it can grow fine trees, although the

8

provenance appears not to be good. Management this century has included successful regeneration of many of the overmature 18th century beech stands, notably along the 1750 Grand Avenue which had deteriorated through drought, beech-snap disease and age; and, near the Eight Walks centrepiece, by using a group shelterwood system (R. Budden, personal communication).

Compartments 74b and 75b received a more uniform regeneration felling of beech, taking advantage of advance natural regeneration during the past 25 years and associated in part with clearing up after the gale in January 1990. Some older groups of regeneration are becoming diverse in canopy structure and age (Plate 2).

The old stands are generally too even in age and the plan now is to break up the older age classes and achieve diversity by a mix of natural seeding and planting. The best stands are good examples of converting old beechwoods by a mixture of uniform and group shelterwood to diverse age and canopy structure by natural regeneration, but much patience is needed to achieve adequate natural regeneration, followed by some respacing. The high value of Savernake Forest for recreation, wildlife and timber production will be greatly enhanced in the future.

Slindon Park, West Sussex

In 1978, at Slindon, owned by The National Trust, Aldhous found 'plentiful' natural regeneration under fine mature beech which had been thinned moderately from time to time since 1950 (Aldhous, 1981). The forest floor had been scarified before the fall of heavy beech masts in 1970 and 1976. In 1978 some 20% of the older beech were severely affected or killed by drought and beech bark disease, hence were felled. Sadly the overstorey and the regeneration were ruined by the severe storm of 1987.

Windsor Forest, Berkshire

The Crown Estate has one of the most impressive examples of pedunculate oak natural regeneration in Britain. In both Cranbourne Wood (Cpt. 107) and High Standing Hill Wood (Cpt. 21d) the fine regeneration is now (1995) 6-8 m tall, and very dense (Plate 3). The old overwood was felled during World Wars I and II.

Natural regeneration appeared in 1962 at a density of $20\,000–25\,000$ ha^{-1}. Seeding losses due to natural causes, and mortality due to suppression by dominants, followed by a recent cleaning, reduced the density to an acceptable 6000 live quality stems ha^{-1} in 1992. Re-spacings will be done as necessary, while maintaining stem and crown density to restrict direct light and the formation of epicormic growth.

Details of the early treatments applied were not recorded, but Peter Garthwaite (1972) describes some of the techniques of establishment used by Robert Lindsay who was Director of Forestry when these compartments were established. Acorns were often broadcast to boost natural seed supplies, and a large rotovator was usually used to ensure this seed was buried. Oak seedbearers were usually retained, but the number, and the length of time they were retained, is not known. It may be that these oak crops were established with very little shelter from an overstorey (F.G. Stickler, personal communication).

Wakefield, Northamptonshire

In 1982 Peter Garthwaite made an interesting attempt to manage ash on a shelterwood system. Most of the wood was mixed ash, oak, lime and sycamore coppice 30-50 years old, with some oak and ash standards. A heavy thinning was done in compartment 1 of 14 ha reducing the basal area to 19 m^2 ha^{-1}. The sys-

9

tem was continued until 1987 when the October storm in southern England caused a glut in the market for ash so that felling was suspended. During this period the majority of compartments 1-6 (79 ha) had been selectively thinned. The response has been quite dramatic both on the trees remaining and on the extent of ash natural regeneration. The latter is entirely dependent upon light availability, there being no shortage of viable seed from the standing ash. There has been little or no oak regeneration but some sycamore where seed trees exist nearby. John Newcomb took over the management in 1988 and the thinning recommenced in 1989-90 when a further 45 ha was worked. About 25 ha remain to be thinned as soon as the market for ash improves.

Group shelterwood

In the lowlands of England, the examples of group shelterwood systems have tended to merge with uniform shelterwood systems. Management has been more informal than in Europe, and use of seeding, secondary and final fellings and precise regeneration periods are unusual. The following three adaptations are noteworthy.

Forest of Dean, Gloucestershire

Here the regeneration and management regime followed by the Forestry Commission for 1200 ha of broadleaves (Joslin, 1982) was based on 'group shelterwood'. Seeding fellings, removing 60% of the *volume* were made to create and enlarge groups, followed 5 to 7 years later by one or more secondary fellings. The timing of the final felling depended on the progress of regeneration, amenity and other considerations. After 11 years of applying this system, 12% of the area was successfully regenerated, and 48% stocked with advance regeneration. Many

good stands have been established by this low-cost regime despite some sheep browsing. However, in some areas the density of oak and beech regeneration can still be rather sparse, with birch and coppice regrowth predominating. Hopefully, within this low-grade matrix there are sufficient oak seedlings to form a final stand. The use of the coppice regrowth as a nurse to such seedlings requires careful timing of cleanings and respacings, if the oak seedlings are not to be overtopped. More recent management of this part of the Forest is probably best classified as 'uniform shelterwood' (J. Everard, personal communication). In summary, the system is used to regenerate broadleaves, but is described as 'shelterwood with retentions'. The size of regeneration unit is 1 ha in the Conservation Working Circle, and up to 5 ha in the Production Working Circle. Seeding fellings now aim to leave 60% *canopy*.

Wyre Forest, north Worcestershire and south-east Shropshire

Wyre contains the remnants of a former royal forest which later came into private ownership. Now, much reduced in size by clearance and modified by reforestation, it still represents one of the largest surviving areas of ancient broadleaved woodland in lowland Britain. Part is owned privately, many of the areas being designated as Sites of Special Scientific Interest or National Nature Reserves, and largely managed by English Nature. Other parts are owned and managed by the Forestry Commission.

The area managed by English Nature, some 570 ha, consists largely of stored coppice sessile oak, mainly 40-50 years in age with some up to 100 years old, mostly with little productive understorey. There is a range of soil conditions, mainly acidic and often poor in nutrients, and the field layer is varied. Throughout this century the original coppices have grown into high forest of oak, plus a limited number of other species which have become adapted to this type of woodland condition. Some of the less common broadleaved species are responding to management and their numbers are increasing.

The main aim of management is to create high forest in 90 to 100 years with a diverse structure instead of the present random range of age classes, about half by the group shelterwood method; but about one-third is reserved as pure coppice on a 30-year cycle (coupes about 1 ha in area, 3.5 ha cut each year); the remainder will include coppice with standards, and some areas of limited silvicultural treatment. Much attention is given to sensitive edge treatment of rides, roads and pathways. In any case, owing to changes in soil and site conditions, part will become diverse in structure during the next century (J. Robinson, personal communication).

In Shelf Held Coppice, much of the conversion from unbalanced age classes to more diverse conditions of age classes and size classes is planned by group selection felling (see Chapter 3) and regenerating by natural seedlings or coppice regrowth. The system is being used with the expectation that it will be worth repeating throughout one half of the Forest. In the 1980s, a compartment of 50 to 60-year-old sessile oak derived from stored coppice was heavily thinned to encourage crown development and seed production. Seventeen groups, each of about 30 m diameter (0.07 ha), were felled in 1985; in 1986 there was an abundance of oak seedlings, approximately 10 per m² (Pryor, 1985). Subsequently, six larger groups of about 0.5 ha have been felled and fenced each year in the 40 to 90-year-old stands. The success of the restocking has depended largely on site condition, not only with oak but also with other broadleaved species, notably birch. Within the fenced groups (Plate 4), the natural regeneration depends largely on the soil fertility and on the varying field layer (bracken, heather, bilberry and excessive bramble) and the invasion of birch. Throughout much of the woodland there is good regeneration of oak, but unless fenced it is continually damaged by fallow deer; and even after 6 years is rarely taller than a few centimetres.

Queen Wood, Watlington Forest, The Chilterns, Oxfordshire

The wood demonstrates several successful examples of 'group regeneration' of beech. In 1945, 27-36 m diameter groups were created by felling, resulting in adequate beech natural regeneration around the perimeters; the groups were too large and prevented beech mast reaching the centres (Brown, 1953). Queen Wood was purchased by the Forestry Commission in 1947 as a demonstration area for beech regeneration. By then, the clearings were occupied by a variety of low shrubs and tall herbs, and few beech seedlings. In 1952 and 1961 parts of the mature and over-mature broadleaves, predominantly beech, were felled in strips and replanted mainly with beech but also with some oak and other broadleaves. More recently, coupes of varying shape and size but typically 0.5-1.0 ha were created by group selection fellings in some of the poorer stands and successfully restocked using treeshelters mainly containing beech but also oak and wild cherry. Despite lack of support from natural seeding, and some damage by deer and adjacent windthrow in January 1990, the foregoing are commendable examples of conversion of mature and over-mature beechwoods. Limited enclosure of small coupes or groups in shelterwood stands is intended in order to benefit from future beech masts (K. Wallis, personal communication.). This example could be termed either group shelterwood or group selection.

Use in Britain : conifers

Uniform and group shelterwood

In the uplands and heathlands of eastern Scotland, in wind zones 3-5, the mainly uniform shelterwood system has been successful on Scots pine natural regeneration on podzols, where *Vaccinium* spp. are dominant over the forest floor. Besides Seafield Estate (notably Curr and Grantown Woods), examples are Glen Tanar Estate, Craigvinean and The Hermitage.

Glen Tanar, Aberdeenshire

Since 1970, Michael Bruce's native pinewood near Aboyne has applied both the uniform shelterwood system using scarification and small group regeneration fellings of 0.3 ha — as irregular shelterwood — in stands aged 150-170 years. The success of natural regeneration in extensive clearings had been well demonstrated several times in the recorded history: following heavy selective fellings from 1810 to 1840, protected from deer until 1865, and following an extensive severe fire in 1920 and after the 1953 storm damage (Edwards, 1981; Miller and Ross, 1990; I. Ross, personal communication). Stands were prepared for regeneration by thinning in the late pole stage to make seed trees windfirm. The group regeneration has suffered from severe deer browsing and the second stage of treating this as irregular shelterwood has had to be postponed. The two stands treated by uniform seeding fellings and mechanical scarification show promising regeneration. It has been found that a stocking of 100 seed trees ha^{-1} can cast excessive shade if crowns are well developed.

The most successful regeneration at Glen Tanar, extending to over 100 ha, has taken place alongside the pinewood on heather moor treated by muirburn progressively over 20-30 years. Indications are that regeneration groups for Scots pine may need to be extensive in size or of few seed trees per hectare to provide adequate light. A degree of scarifying to provide a regeneration surface is necessary to overcome the effects of *Calluna* and *Sphagnum* mosses (Low, 1988). The appropriate structure may evolve after continued shelterwood experience and after research on light requirements. The forest manager since 1977 has been Irvine Ross.

Craigvinean, Perthshire

Craigvinean is an extensive Forest Enterprise forest, about 1 mile (1½ km) west of Dunkeld. It adjoins the upper side of The Hermitage Wood, described below. Compartment 3040e (2.9 ha) comprises mature Douglas fir at the eastern end with younger planting of the same species in P58 and P80. Much of the old stand has produced natural regeneration of mixed ages and heights, in effect being an unplanned variation of group and uniform shelterwood systems. The 1980 stands were formed by planting in gaps following windthrow. The appearance now is of irregular shelterwood. The management plan is to thin the 1958 stands, and to respace the understorey of natural regeneration. The system will be extended to a further 113 ha in Craigvinean to achieve uneven-aged stands in Sitka spruce, Norway spruce, Douglas fir and larch. In part of the adjacent compartment 3040g with old Scots pine, beech and oak and younger Douglas fir, the management plan is to maintain diversity of species and structure.

In 1993, Craigvinean Forest (Forest Enterprise District Manager, Charles Taylor) won the new 'Landscape Institute Award' for the design plan.

The Hermitage Wood, Dunkeld

Alongside the River Braan, a tributary of the River Tay, about 1 mile (1½ km) west of Dunkeld, lies The Hermitage Wood, owned by

The National Trust for Scotland. It comprises about 15 ha of mixed conifers and broadleaves of great beauty and wildlife interest. The south-west upper part (compartment 4, 4.3 ha) contains stands of large Douglas fir, Norway spruce and Scots pine 70-80 years old, some standing above sporadically formed groups and single trees of naturally regenerated Douglas fir (0.2-4.0 m in height) with smaller and less thriving Norway spruce. These are examples of unplanned variants of both uneven-aged and even-aged shelterwood. Slightly lower down the slope are small groups of mid-rotation Douglas fir and Norway spruce, with a few grand fir, of varying ages believed to have been naturally regenerated (Plate 5).

Grampian and Tayside Regions

During 1960-1970, in the Grampian and Tayside regions of Scotland, 40-year-old larch stands were successfully underplanted on a 5 to 10-year regeneration period by the Forestry Commission under the influence of Frank Oliver and Morley Penistan (see Appendix 5), using Douglas fir, grand fir, western hemlock and Norway spruce. Removal of the upper storey was often delayed owing to low demand for larch sawlogs and this occasionally resulted in two-storied high forest. The system fell into disuse due to:

- reduced intensity of supervision;
- changes in extraction methods;
- loss of skilled fellers;
- improved weed control in clear cutting by use of herbicides;
- a preference for Sitka spruce which did not require protection of an overwood.

However, in England the shelterwood system has been unsuccessful with Japanese larch, aged about 40-50 years on brown earths, when aimed at using natural regeneration, e.g. at Grizedale, for reasons advanced by Paterson (1990):

1. too short a period for preparation and isolation of seed trees and thinning on boundaries;
2. poor provenance of original stand;
3. climatic conditions causing frequent failure of cone crops;
4. competition from *Deschampsia flexuosa* sward;
5. inadequate protection against deer browse.

Treatment resulted in sparse inadequate stocking of regeneration.

In the lowlands of England, three examples of mainly uniform shelterwood, using conifer natural regeneration are at Windsor, Swinley and Wyre.

Windsor Forest, Berkshire

On the Crown Estate in High Standing Hill Wood is an impressive example of natural regeneration of grand fir managed under a more or less uniform shelterwood system (Plate 6). Following heavy windthrow in January 1990, a P52 stand of grand fir was thinned and the branchwood cleared in spring 1990. This coincided with a good mast, which during 1990-1991 led to dense natural regeneration, now (1995) 5 years old (F.G. Stickler, personal communication). The overwood, which now stands at 575 stems ha^{-1}, will be progressively removed. A thriving and inexpensive new stand will be gained by skilled management of this timely use of natural regeneration.

Crown Estate, Swinley

There are fine examples of Scots pine growing on Bagshot heath, established over a period from 1950 to 1970 under the uniform shelterwood system (Plate 7), currently in use to restock areas devastated by the storms of 1987 and 1990.

Scarification is undertaken to encourage germination, which typically amounts to about 25 000 seedlings ha^{-1} following removal of the parent trees. Costly early respacing is unnecessary due to natural suppression and emergence of dominants; so stands are left untouched for 25 years. Following an early thinning to remove dead and suppressed stems, stocking is likely to be about 5000 stems ha^{-1}. Periodic thinning is practised and regeneration fellings are commenced at age 55. Final felling is carried out when stands are fully stocked and the new crop is about 1 m tall. These fine examples of uniform shelterwood system have proved to be more profitable, more windfirm, and of better quality (straighter and cleaner poles, naturally pruned) than planted stands. The marketing of produce is facilitated by a good local demand for transmission poles (F.G. Stickler, personal communication).

Wyre Forest

Within the Forest Enterprise management of part of this ancient forest, a stand of 17 ha of P26 Douglas fir which suffered severe windthrow in 1974 was followed that year by natural regeneration of Douglas fir (with some Corsican pine and European larch) and mixed broadleaves, mainly birch. Further seeding continued. In 1988 the overstorey was lightly thinned, removing about 50 stems ha^{-1}. The result (1995) is a heavily stocked thriving example of shelterwood. Respacing is soon to be undertaken and final felling of the overwood will follow in due course.

Conclusions on shelterwood systems

1. *Application to light-demanding conifers.* Shelterwood systems can be widely applied to light-demanding conifers provided that the windthrow hazard classification of the site does not exceed 3 (or perhaps 4 with stand preparation) and the soil is freely drained.

2. *Regeneration in large areas.* Foresters on the Continent, when having to regenerate large areas of conifer forest or broadleaved woodland, have turned to the uniform shelterwood system which was designed to restock large areas with regular even-aged stands like those produced through the clear cutting system. This system can work in Britain and examples are provided by the Scots pine and pedunculate oak on the Crown Estate at Windsor, pedunculate oak in the Forest of Dean and beech at Slindon (although the last named has been lost by windthrow). The small areas of grand fir at Windsor and Douglas fir in Wyre Forest were responses to windthrow in the old stand.

3. *Regeneration: influence of combination of soil and species.* The relatively strict sequence of regeneration fellings, i.e. seeding, secondary and final, are used for Scots pine at Windsor, where the favourable combination of soil and species has prompted use of the uniform shelterwood system to produce abundant regeneration which can be selectively grown on as transmission poles for a demanding but profitable market. (This was the practice followed historically on the Seafield Estate, Strathspey.) Elsewhere, regeneration fellings have followed a less formal pattern, except in the case of recent treatment of oak and beech in the Forest of Dean.

4. *Regeneration fellings.* In the group shelterwood system the regeneration fellings are used to enlarge groups of regeneration so that eventually they coalesce, but so far British foresters have used them in an informal and even short-term manner. This system, as adapted to British conditions, appears suited to small mixed woods provided they are sheltered from wind, and the soils are light to medium in texture and quite deep. Sometimes there is a distinct feeling that the owners and foresters are on the verge of using variants of the irregular shelterwood system and this is the case in The Hermitage Wood near Dunkeld, and parts of the Glen Tanar native pinewoods. When using the irregular shelterwood system it is not necessary to specify the regeneration period closely, nor is the rotation

fixed; the seedbearers can be left until the current annual increment falls below an acceptable level. But irregular shelterwood produces a wood or forest that is close to group selection, and the owner or forester might consider using continuous inventory of three size classes to regulate yield.

5. *Small stands.* In parts of Britain there are admirable small stands of large old broadleaves and conifer species on sheltered sites (the old beeches at Savernake provide a good example). The group shelterwood system has already been proved useful in several of these and could be used more widely to keep representatives of the old stands and enable the next generation to conserve their pool of genes.

6. *Silvicultural prescriptions.* The number of seedbearers to be retained in a seeding felling for the uniform shelterwood and group shelterwood systems can only be finally determined by local experience. As a guide, if maturing stands of the major species used in Britain are stocked at 300-500 stems ha^{-1}, the canopy is too dense for young plants of light-demanders to survive for long; the seeding felling should remove more than half the old stand, leaving 75 to 120 seedbearers of oak, ash, birch, Scots pine or Sitka spruce. As the regeneration (whether natural, direct seeded or planted) becomes established, secondary and final fellings are made. For the shade-enduring and moderately shade-enduring species — beech, sycamore, grand fir, Norway spruce, Douglas fir, western hemlock and western red cedar — a seeding felling should retain seedbearers of 150 to 200 trees ha^{-1}.

7. *Thinning prescriptions.* In uniform shelterwood, stands should be prepared by heavy selection crown thinnings to make seedbearers more stable. In group shelterwood, thinning around groups must be undertaken when required. If 'advance growth' of shade-enduring natural seedlings appears in groups on the forest floor beneath a canopy of maturing trees stocked at 300-500 stems ha^{-1}, reducing it to around 200 trees should encourage appearance of the shade-bearers; and further reducing the stocking of the old trees to 100 ha^{-1} should induce light-demanders to appear. It is important that these general prescriptions should be tested on representative trial areas before embarking on operations using the shelterwood systems. It will also be seen that controlling the stocking of the seedbearers or overstorey provides the forester with control of the composition of mixtures. Co-ordination of fellings with mast years should be attempted.

8. *Size of the regeneration block.* The areas treated by the group shelterwood system have varied from 10 to 50 ha, which is a reason for suggesting that the system could be adapted to the conditions in small woods. Scope is considerable in Britain's eastern pinewoods and birchwoods generally. It is unlikely to be of value in upland spruce forests because of instability in seedbearers on wet soils.

9. *Protection.* Because large (and perhaps small) mammals prefer feeding in small clearings surrounded by taller stands which provide cover, regeneration tends to suffer relatively greater damage on coupes of up to 2 ha unless the numbers of deer and other animals are controlled or fencing is erected, or both measures are taken. In Wyre Forest, fallow deer browsed unprotected plants of oak to a stunted condition and at Glen Tanar Forest unprotected native Scots pine regeneration is browsed by red or roe deer down to the top level of the heather sward. Large groups tend to have greater weed growth in the centre of the clearing and fewer seedlings, while smaller groups have a long perimeter of edge trees for their area and may suffer from more endemic wind damage. The success of the group shelterwood system in restocking the whole area depends on being able to enlarge the initial clearings by further regeneration fellings around their edges so that the individual groups coalesce. If this process is slow, the new stand becomes somewhat irregular but this is corrected when cleanings and thinnings are done.

10. *Rotation.* In the shelterwood systems the regeneration period is usually 5 to 10 years for Scots pine and 20 to 30 years for beech and oak. If the rotation includes the period for regeneration, the rotation for average yield classes will total 60 to 65 or more years for Scots pine and 80 to 100 years or more for beech and oak. In the group shelterwood system the rotation may be longer unless the groups can be enlarged quite rapidly. The drawback of a lengthened rotation can usually be offset by a greater timber value for the seedbearers and an extended period of having the benefits of a diverse structure.

11. *Factors causing difficulty in applying the shelterwood systems.* Experience in the north-east of Scotland during 1960 to 1970 suggested that the conversion of pure stands of larch by underplanting them with several conifer species could run into difficulty through delayed removal of the overstorey, changing methods of harvesting, a preference for species that did not thrive under a larch overstorey, and reduced intensity of supervision. These drawbacks also apply to the creation of two-storied high forest (see Chapter 5). The length of rotation can exceed the rotation of maximum mean annual increment (MAI) by 15 or more years, entailing some loss of financial performance if these criteria and timber production revenues are the only ones measured and valued.

12. *Factors leading to success with the shelterwood systems.* If large logs of the principal species are in good demand in the long term, seed production of the desired species regular and plentiful, weed growth sparce, and regeneration appears readily, the shelterwood systems can provide an efficient means of forming new stands. Moreover, the appearance of an area of woodland or forest is attractive because the seedbearers give enhanced height and stature to the temporary two-storied stands. But the effect does not last and a return is made to the aspect of regular more or less even-aged stands, sometimes with a few old standards reserved for special markets.

Chapter 3
The group selection system

Introduction

In the group selection system the growing stock of trees is arranged in groups of varying dimensions appropriate to the requirements of each species: small for shade-tolerant species, and larger for light-demanders. These groups are dispersed through the forest to form a continuous mosaic, so that a recently regenerated group of (say) Norway spruce could adjoin a maturing group of Douglas fir, a pole-stage group of beech, and a thicket-stage group of ash. There will be interaction between these various groups; and to ensure that they keep their identities for tending, protection, yield control and harvesting, the dimensions corresponding to these areas are suggested in Tables 3.1 and 3.2. Access to the groups is provided by a network of rides and extraction paths, and the groups themselves may be established according to a formal pattern or, more commonly, on a less formal layout.

The formation of such a forest may start either by converting existing stands of pure, even-aged, uniform canopies, or by restoring exploited 'derelict woodland' which contains scrub, untended groups of regeneration, a few productive stands, single older trees that were too small or too low quality for exploitation, and bare unstocked ground. In both cases the objective of conversion to the group selection system is to create productive forest which is diverse in structure and appearance, uneven-aged, provides diverse habitat for wildlife, is suitable for field sports and recreation, and produces a sustained yield of timber and other benefits in perpetuity.

The advantages of the system according to Matthews (1989) are: flexible and particularly well-suited to small stands where intensive working and close supervision are possible; accommodating a wide variety of species ranging from light-demanders, moderate shade-bearers to the shade-tolerant species. Aesthetically the open glades, thickets and tall trees are pleasing. The disadvantages are: skill is needed in selecting groups of trees in the existing stand for retention; felling, extracting, regenerating and tending are scattered and on a small-scale. In short, experienced and knowledgeable supervision is required. The costs are likely to be higher than those in a comparable area of even-aged forest; control of browsing and bark-stripping mammals is more difficult and damage done can be more severe; and timber quality problems can arise from heavy branching on edge trees.

Use in Britain: broadleaves

The Census of English Woodlands taken between 1947 and 1949 revealed the dire condition of substantial areas of broadleaved woodland, largely as a result of selective felling during World Wars I and II and of intervening periods of neglect, or of management mainly for field sports. In 1950 the Forestry Commission tested three methods for converting unproductive, chiefly broadleaved stands to high forest (Wood, 1950):

1. clear cutting and restocking with broadleaved species, either pure or in mixtures;

2. new planting under the shelter of existing trees or in strips and groups cleared through degraded woodland;

3. enrichment with single trees and small groups of commercial species, favouring the best trees of the existing stand.

Table 3.1 Dimensions of groups for different species

Species	Rotation [a] (years)	Crown diameter (m)	Crown projection area (m²)	Size of square plot (m²)
Douglas fir	50-60	6	28	36
Ash and sycamore	60	9-10	64-78	81
Oak	100	14	164	196

[a] Strictly speaking, group selection does not have a 'rotation'; the criterion is the exploitable final tree diameter aimed for.

To enlarge the table and adapt it for local use, make measurements of the crown diameters and crown projection areas for mature trees of the desired species in a given wood or forest, and then decide on the desired number of final crop trees in each group.

Table 3.2 Dimensions of clearings to provide growing space for trees of final size. (Sources: Matthews, 1986, 1989)

Diameter of group (m)	Area (ha)	Number of plants (2 x 2 m spacing)	Number of trees of final size		
			Douglas fir	Ash, sycamore	Oak
11-13	0.01	25-35	3	1	1
15-17	0.02	45-55	5	2	1
19-21	0.03	70-85	8	4	2
22-24	0.04	95-115	11	5	2
25-26	0.05	120-130	14	6	3
27-28	0.06	145-155	16	7	3
29-30	0.07	165-175	18	8	4
31-32	0.08	180-200	21	9	4
33-34	0.09	215-230	24	10	5
35-36	0.10	240-255	27	12	5
37-38	0.11	270-285	30	13	6
39-40	0.12	300-315	33	15	6
41	0.13	330	36	16	7
42-43	0.14	345-365	38	17	7
44	0.15	380	42	19	8
45-46	0.16	400	44	20	9
47	0.17	435	48	21	9
48-49	0.18	450-470	50	22	10
50-51	0.20	490-510	54	24	15
62	0.30	755	83	37	20
72	0.40	1020	113	50	25
80	0.50	1255	139	62	30
88	0.60	1520	169	75	32
90	0.63	1590	177	78	–

The results of this work became the basis of recommendations for improving unproductive State and private stands in the lowlands (Wood *et al.*, 1967; Evans, 1984). At this time, much use was also made of birch as an overwood to establish beech on thin chalk downland soils in southern England; also of 2 row/2 row or 3 row/3 row mixtures of larch/oak or Scots pine/beech in cleared areas.

18

Plate 1. *Natural regeneration of pedunculate oak and beech under the uniform shelterwood system at Churchill East, Forest of Dean.* (41312)

Plate 2. *Beech natural regeneration at Savernake Forest, Wiltshire. Older groups of regeneration are becoming diverse in canopy structure and age.* (TOM BUCHANAN)

Plate 3. *Pedunculate oak natural regeneration at High Standing Hill Wood, Windsor Forest. The fine dense regeneration is now 5–6 m tall.* (41314)

Plate 4. Natural regeneration of oak at Wyre Forest. Fencing has improved the success of natural regeneration by excluding mammals but the birch is intrusive. (CYRIL HART)

Plate 5. Douglas fir and Norway spruce in a group shelterwood system at The Hermitage Wood, near Dunkeld, of great beauty and wildlife interest. (ANTHONY HART)

Plate 6. Impressive natural regeneration of grand fir in a uniform shelterwood system at High Standing Hill Wood, Windsor Forest. (41313)

Plate 7. *Fine Scots pine natural regeneration under a uniform shelterwood system at the Crown Estate, Swinley.* (41315)

Plate 8. *Beech natural regeneration under 110-year-old trees at Workmans Wood, Ebworth, Gloucestershire: an impressive example of continuing group selection of broadleaves.* (41270)

Plate 9. *European larch in a superb stand at Cawdor Big Wood, near Nairn.* (CYRIL HART)

Plate 10. *Oak trees in fog at Cawdor Big Wood, near Nairn. This famous Scottish wood of great scenic beauty is predominantly pedunculate and sessile oak with some mixed stands of conifers.* (ALAN WATSON)

Plate 11. *The Glentress Trial, Glentress Forest, near Peebles: a conversion of conifer stands from uniform even-aged clear cutting system to uneven-aged group selection, producing a wide range of benefits including high standard of amenity, nature conservation and forest recreation.* (CYRIL HART)

Plate 12. *Conversion of conifers to group selection system at Corrour Forest, Inverness-shire, showing diverse stand structure initiated in compartment 3.* (FELIX KARTHAUS)

Plate 13. *Old Scots pine at Faskally Wood, near Pitlochry, Perthshire. An example of conversion by M. L. Anderson and others towards group selection in conifers.* (ANTHONY HART)

Plate 14. *Benevean Wood in Glen Affric, Inverness-shire: an example of group or random regeneration of indigenous Scots pine.* (39518)

Plate 15. *Douglas fir naturally regenerating under mature crop at Diosgydd, Gwynedd: an example of conversion of conifer plantations to group selection.* (41265)

Plate 16. *Sitka spruce and beech regeneration under mature larch at Nant BH, Gwynedd. Note carpet of bilberry.* (41267)

Plate 17. *Application of a shelterwood-cum-group selection system to conifers at Longleat, Wiltshire, showing natural regeneration under Douglas fir.* (41275)

Plate 18. *Prolific natural regeneration of western hemlock in a single tree selection system at Kyloe Wood, south of Berwick-on-Tweed, Northumberland.* (H. WHITNEY MCIVER)

Plate 20. *Hamsterley Forest: smaller scale restructuring.* (38812)

Plate 19. *Kielder Forest: restructuring for increasingly multiple purpose objectives.* (39879)

Plate 21. *Group regeneration of beech in the Chilterns showing a well-established group of young trees in an opening in the canopy of mature beech.* (E7785)

Plate 22. *A mixed storey formed by regenerating beech in the Chilterns.* (E10357)

Plate 23. *Natural regeneration under a stand of c. 150-year-old beech in the Chilterns: an example of restructuring of beechwoods by group regeneration.* (10244)

In the regeneration of such woodlands, adaptations of the group shelterwood system and the group selection system have been used more frequently than other alternative systems. The motives have been to achieve forest cover for reasons of silviculture, protection or aesthetic and environmental benefit. The foresters concerned have been enthusiastic and patient, also opportunistic and flexible in management, not always adhering to any formal system, so that it is difficult to classify some of the examples because distinctions between the variants have become blurred.

Group selection is a term that has been widely used in Britain and loosely applied to almost any regeneration obtained by clearing areas in groups, but in this Bulletin the term refers to systems in which the management area is subdivided into groups or components that are usually even-aged and have one storey. A group selection stand differs from a single tree selection stand (see Chapter 4) in that a time comes when all the trees in a group or component must be removed because they are judged mature, whereas in single tree selection working, trees judged to be mature are felled singly through the forest or section of a forest. In group selection there is still a shelterwood notion: an older stand provides protection for young crops that are developing alongside and the period of side shelter may be as long as 30 years or more. It differs from a single tree selection stand in that regeneration is tended in *groups*, which take the place of individual trees. The individual groups will not differ much in structure and average age but the group selection structure will be clearly visible overall as small stands varying in size, age and species. In contrast to the shelterwood group system, the size of each group or component is fixed at the time of regeneration, instead of being steadily enlarged so that the groups coalesce to form one large stand.

The group selection system has been used more frequently (Table 3.3) than the group shelterwood system because long or indefinite regeneration periods have been adopted due to poor initial regeneration. Aldhous (1981), having visited many beechwoods in southern England, concluded that the only successful method to obtain natural regeneration was to secure advance regeneration and fell only where it is well established, an assertion confirmed by some of the following fine woodlands.

Ebworth, Gloucestershire

Many fine stands of beech are growing on several private estates in the Cotswolds. Most notably, good quality beech is grown in an environmentally sensitive manner at Ebworth, owned since 1989 by the National Trust and managed by English Nature with the continued assistance of the donor, John Workman OBE. Workmans Wood, occupying 120 ha on steep slopes, is an ancient semi-natural beechwood, generally high forest of diverse age and size, with trees of ages from newly seeded up to about 200 years old. The only current lack is that of 50 to 150-year-old trees. It is the most impressive example of continuing 'group selection' of broadleaves in Britain, comprising high quality timber production while achieving continuous forest cover and maintaining rich and diverse wildlife interest (Plate 8).

The basis of the silviculture is securing advance natural regeneration and, when it is well established, felling the mature trees over the regeneration. Where there has been a gap in the beech canopy, sycamore and ash regeneration may have come in initially, but usually sufficient beech is awaited before undertaking small group fellings. A few potentially fine ash which benefit from mixture with other broadleaves are welcomed. Occasionally beech regeneration will appear when the overstorey is not mature (100 years), in which case thinnings are made to favour this, and eventually the overstorey may be felled before it is fully mature to ensure that the advance regeneration does not suffer. Typically, it takes around 30 years to naturally regenerate a stand, and towards the end of this period some infilling with beech transplants may be necessary. No weeding is done

Table 3.3 The location of stands treated by the group selection system

	Wind zone [a]	Site	Species	Conversion period
England				
Ebworth Estate, Gloucestershire Workmans Wood	3-4	Jurassic limestone	Broadleaved	40 years
Hockeridge Estate, Hertfordshire	2		Mixed	
Cirencester Park, Gloucestershire	1	Jurassic limestone	Broadleaved	50 years
Dartington Estate, Devon	3	South-west peninsula	Conifers	
Longleat Estate, Wiltshire	2	Lower Greensand	Conifers	45 years
Tavistock, Devon	3-4	Medium to high fertility	Conifers	54 years
Wales				
Cefn Llwyd Forest, Bala	5	Brown earths	Conifers	
Coed y Brenin, Dolgellau	5	Brown earths	Conifers	
Ffrwdgrech Woodlands, Brecon	3	Brown earths	Conifers	
Clocaenog Forest, north-east Wales	5	Brown earths	Conifers	
Scotland				
Bowhill and Eildon Woods, Borders	5-6	Eastern, brown earths and surface-water gleys	Mixed	
Cawdor Big Wood, Nairn	4	Eastern, brown earths	Mixed	
Glentress Forest, Peebles	5-6	Eastern, brown earths and surface-water gleys	Conifers	60 years
Corrour Forest, Inverness-shire	6-7	High moorland	Conifers	
Drumlanrig Estate, Thornhill	6	Western, brown earths and surface-water gleys	Mixed	
Faskally Wood, Pitlochry	3	Eastern, brown earths and surface-water gleys	Conifers	
Benevean Wood, Affric Forest	5	Northern, wet heath	Conifers	70 years

[a] Wind zone describes the regional windiness for the site; values obtained from Quine and White (1993) and Quine (personal communications for areas in SE England). See Glossary 1 for further definition.

as ground vegetation is controlled by manipulation of the overstorey but the regeneration is rigorously cleaned once the overstorey has been removed, and secondary species are retained to nurse the beech. Respacing is generally completed by the 15th year. The groups are usually less than 0.3 ha in size.

The natural regeneration is mainly of beech of good genetic stock with some planting from local sources, thus operating an uneven-aged system of groups of trees of different ages. The whole concept is based on fostering regeneration, i.e. observing where beech seedlings are appearing and gradually felling back from these initial patches, allowing side-light to penetrate below the canopy and so provide the critical conditions essential for successful establishment and early growth of beech seedlings. The long-term objective is sustained yield from continuous forest cover. The notable example at Ebworth has been achieved by John Workman over some 40 years by skilled, patient and opportunist management in the face of many problems: damage by wood-pigeon, grey squirrel, wood mice, fallow and roe deer, excessive bramble and wild clematis, and extremes of temperature (Workman, 1986). Among relevant lessons learned are:

- voles respace regeneration;

- badgers aid regeneration by disturbing the forest floor;

- if the canopy is too dense, the forest floor is clean and inhospitable, but if opened too much dense bramble and grass smother the seedlings;

- dog's mercury and nettle hinder regeneration.

The balance is precarious and depends on intimate knowledge of the overstorey and the site. The result of management is a woodland heritage of national renown: evidence of one man's vision and commitment now partnered by the resources of an enlightened national organisation, growing fine quality broadleaved timber, and making special provision for landscape, public access, education and wildlife.

In 1993, John Workman won one of the two first national Forestry Authority Awards identifying England's best forestry.

Since the end of the World War II, J. E. Garfitt (see Appendix 5), following Ray Bourne (see Appendix 5) has been a vigorous and successful designer of variants of the group selection system, particularly for broadleaves, in mid and southern lowland England. The essence of Garfitt's system is that the trees should be allowed to grow in full light, the groups being a certain minimum size, defined as having a diameter at least one-and-a-half times the height of the surrounding stand. In most conditions and on most soils in lowland England and Wales the optimum size is usually between 0.1 and 0.5 ha. Except where total reliance is placed on natural regeneration, the distribution of the species within such groups is controlled by the forester. Since the groups consist of more or less even-aged trees, the distribution of the age and size classes throughout the forest is determined by the groups which take the place of individual stems in the single tree selection system (see Chapter 4). In group selection it is convenient to avoid small annual fellings and plantings, and to work on a 5- or 10-year cycle. The choice of this cycle will determine the extent of the felling which is to be carried out in one year. This will be made up of a number of groups in the forest. Co-ordination of fellings with mast years should be attempted.

Garfitt (1984) discusses application of his system to three cases of conversion:

- from uniform even-aged woodland

- from unmanaged woodland

- from scrub.

The result of the application will be the creation of a forest which, once established, will not change overall. Individual parts will go through the familiar stages of young crop, thicket, young pole stage, pole stage, and large trees; but the forest as a whole will remain essentially the same, all the constituents being constant in the proportion of ground that they occupy. With the limited size of group envisaged, at any one point the full range of size classes will be visible, producing effects desired both from nature conservation and amenity points of view, that is, open glades, among stately trees of many sizes. At the same time, it will be possible at any stage to initiate changes in the species used and in any mixtures employed; and by judicious manipulation to retain fine specimen trees to a considerable age, to create vistas, to preserve shelter effects and to preserve important ecosystems. Three applications by Garfitt are noted, one at Hockeridge and two at Cirencester Park.

Hockeridge, near Berkhamsted, Hertfordshire

This wood was gifted by Miss Mary Wellesley in 1986 to the Royal Forestry Society of England, Wales and Northern Ireland. Here Garfitt (1953, 1984) developed a variant of the group selection system. Management, begun in 1954, consisted of cleaning and enriching any acceptable beech regeneration, but most was scrub or birch woodland. Garfitt aimed to retain the benefit of shelter and to create an uneven-aged wood of diverse structure through small blocks of contrasting ages; therefore he clear felled and regenerated rectangular areas of 0.4 to 0.6 ha. Of particular benefit has been the extensive internal edges throughout the wood resulting from the small groups, making it ideal for wildlife conservation.

Cirencester Park, Gloucestershire

In the first of the two applications at Cirencester Park, Garfitt (1953) managed considerable areas in which existing regeneration of ash and sycamore occurred in patches. European larch, Scots pine and beech were planted between the patches, using pure groups similar in size to those of the regeneration groups. This involved the removal of existing inferior growth, including hazel underwood. Some fine groups of pole-stage stands have resulted under Arthur Lloyd's management.

In the second application at Cirencester Park, Garfitt (1953) applied a form of group selection in areas where the beech overstorey had been removed in wartime fellings. Clearance of the hazel underwood was essential before planting of beech, European larch and Scots pine. No planting was done under the shade of old hazel or other growth. Management has changed under subsequent regimes but many of the stages in the original system can still be traced, although much of the planted conifer was removed in early thinnings, resulting in a greater proportion of sycamore and ash. Current management is tending towards a form of group shelterwood system leading to final stands of a 'uniform' character. Groups of regeneration are typically 0.05 to 0.1 ha in size, and the range of ages within each group is less than 10 years. The aim of the present management is to spread the felling of the remaining areas of beech overstorey over 20 to 30 years, by which stage all the groups will have merged. The most abundant seedlings are ash and sycamore, but through the selection applied in three cleanings in the first 15 years, the proportion of beech and wild cherry is considerably increased. Ash and sycamore are, in effect, used as a matrix or nurse for the final stand species which are less abundant. Thus Garfitt's original group selection system has been converted into a mixture of shelterwood systems.

In the lowlands of Scotland, two notable examples of attempted and projected conversion of mainly broadleaved woodland towards group selection are: Bowhill and Eildon Woods, and Cawdor Big Wood.

In the neighbourhood of Selkirk and Melrose there are two notable examples of conversion from even-aged to uneven-aged (or more correctly uneven tree size) forestry using the group selection system. Conversion of mainly broadleaved stands (oak, beech, sycamore, ash) surrounding the mansionhouses of His Grace the Duke of Buccleuch at Bowhill and Eildon began in 1926 under the Duke of the time, and continued under the 8th Duke, the present Duke's father, who died in 1973.

Since 1956, under the head forester, Jack Watson, there has been continual establishment of groups of conifers and broadleaves in various sizes of clearings, usually on a 6-year cycle. Groups of the upper storey trees were retained to accentuate the group selection structure which now extends over more than 300 ha and is the largest in Britain (Matthews, 1989). During the 1980s, the number and size of the groups were reduced; and the area of small group plantings spread into adjoining commercial conifer stands, usually following the windthrow of small pockets of trees. Thinning (always light) declined in the 1970s, and did not increase in the 1980s. Along with this, there was a practice of retaining smaller trees without opening out the higher canopy to release them, resulting in many drawn stems and moribund trees. The woods became overstocked partly through underthinning and there was little planting during the 1970s and 1980s; diverse structure was developing but not as planned.

Following Jack Watson's retirement in 1988 after 32 years' distinguished service, Graham Booth was appointed as head forester and began a 3-year thinning cycle, which included the mixed stands tending to irregularity. Attempts were made to open out the woods, leaving trees of diverse sizes and species wherever possible. To date (1995) the diverse structure has been emphasised.

Currently the object of timber production is primary in 83% of the area, and the remainder is managed in the interests of shooting, forest recreation, amenity and shelter. For each of the objectives, the timing and location of forestry operations are variable and important. A long-term working plan (using a 4-year thinning cycle) is being developed, particularly in those areas to be run on mixed uneven-aged principles. The silvicultural systems adopted must be sufficiently flexible to encompass storm damage and allow a minimum of management input. The systems to be used will comprise group selection (80%), single tree selection (10%) and in beech stands irregular shelterwood (10%). Considerations as to choice of system will include rotation, profitability, amenity, landscape, wildlife, sporting, recreation, and the need for sensitivity of management, all dependent on site conditions, the state of existing stands and the need for sustained yield and continuous forest cover.

The Estate's aim is for this diverse structure to amount to about 17% of the total forest area. The total aim for the extent of diverse structure is about 300 ha (Bowhill with Eildon). Group size will be less than 1.0 ha. Planting will be done, but natural regeneration of grand fir, Sitka spruce and sycamore will be accepted.

At both Bowhill and Eildon, stands of beech will be managed on a variant of the irregular shelterwood system, over a period of 50 years, with the aim to continue the amenity benefit to each mansionhouse. At Eildon, a stand of mixed uneven-aged conifers and broadleaves is to be converted to the single tree selection system, to include some planting. Elsewhere the group selection system will be used.

Cawdor Big Wood, near Nairn

Cawdor Big Wood, also called Cawdor Old Wood, lies immediately south of the Castle, owned by Lord Cawdor (the 7th Earl).

Probably the most famous oakwood in Scotland (Goss, 1992), it extends to some 303 ha. It is predominantly pedunculate and sessile oak (a few having been coppiced) but there are some mixed stands of conifers. These include superb stands of European larch, arguably of the best quality in Britain (Plate 9). The Big Wood (Plate 10) lies between, and straddles, the arms of an inverted 'Y' formed by the confluence of two burns flowing through rocky gorges of great scenic beauty and interest.

The main part of the Big Wood is sited on Middle Old Red sandstone conglomerate overlain with fluvio-glacial material which has produced a deep freely drained podzolised brown earth of moderate fertility. The elevation is 60-180 m with a northern aspect. The region has the second coldest climate in Scotland and comes within the lowest rainfall zone in Scotland with a mean annual figure of 768 mm. Frosts are recorded on more than 50 days per year, with early June frosts being not uncommon. The Big Wood experienced gales of storm intensity in 1953, 1961 and February 1989, but extensive damage has not occurred in the oak stands. The vegetation type is oak–birch–juniper association. There are several introduced exotic species.

Maps show the area as a wood as early as 1660 and parts may have been wooded since the period of general cover of the lowlands with natural sessile oakwood sometime after glaciation (Goss, 1992). Parts were once used for arable and pastoral agriculture, with patch farming in places. The planting was probably done by John (or 'Jack') Campbell (1st Baron Cawdor, from 1768, died 1821). Much of the original remnant was natural sessile oak which had been depleted by selective felling and renewed by planting pedunculate oak, Scots pine and European larch, some 200 years ago. The present stands within the Big Wood are mainly from 1830-1850 (oak), with small areas planted between 1859 and 1865 (Norway spruce, Douglas fir, Scots pine and European larch). In 1911, 4 ha of Japanese larch, European larch, Norway spruce and Douglas fir were planted. Other small areas were planted in 1920 and 1938 (Cawdor, 1985).

The Big Wood has not been fully stocked for many decades, so its potential for forestry has not been fully used. The oak is ageing and of relatively poor form, influenced by the use of pedunculate oak introduced by planting. The Big Wood is capable of growing good timber as shown particularly by its sessile oak, Scots pine and European larch, hence its continuity is fully justified as well as for amenity and wildlife conservation. For many decades thought has been given to conversion of it under the group selection system.

In 1967, Professor M. L. Anderson, referring to experiments within the private sector 'concerned with the establishment of an irregular group structure', noted that the Forestry Department in the University of Edinburgh in 1954-55 began such experiments in 'the Old Wood at Cawdor belonging to Lord Cawdor [the 5th Earl] in old oak and birch mixed with conifers'. The objectives of using the group selection system were:

- To bring all parts of the Wood into maximum value production.
- To maintain the existing aesthetic and protective amenities so far as they are compatible with good management.
- To develop the Wood in such a way as to provide the maximum experimental and instructional value.

The Big Wood was divided into 48 compartments, grouped into 6 blocks of about 50 ha each, corresponding to a treatment cycle of 6 years. The intention was to convert it during a period of 120 years by regenerating about 2.5 ha each year in the current block using 25 irregularly spaced small groups. The staff of the Department of Forestry, University of Edinburgh, assisted by students made the annual 100% enumeration, marked the fellings, selected planting groups and made the choice of species.

Anderson's planned 120-year conversion began in 1954-1955 in the old oak, with a group size of about 0.1 ha (Taylor, 1967). He used grand fir or western hemlock and beech in the south part of groups; and Norway spruce, oak, sycamore and European larch in the north, the trees being closely planted in 'nests' of species, about nine in each. Roe deer damage was severe as the groups were not fenced. In 1962 W. A. Fairbairn and W. E. S. Mutch of the staff of the University produced a management plan for 1962-74. Anderson's plan was changed because the ageing Big Wood was suffering from windthrow, the regeneration groups were too small, the planting spacings too close and the species in a single group were too diversified. Accordingly, the conversion period was reduced to 60 years, the annual regeneration allotment doubled, the size of a group increased to 0.4 ha or even more if necessary, and the planting spacing set at 1.4 x 1.4 m but 1.8 x 1.8 m for Douglas fir. Windthrow caused areas to be treated out of phase.

In 1967 under a new management plan the Big Wood was divided into two parts for, mainly, timber production, but with an eighth of the area managed for amenity. From 1970 the 'Anderson trial' was discontinued (Newton, 1986). The groups now require thinning to relieve the young stands.

Today, the Big Wood has a major shortage of recently established and middle-aged trees. However, under the old oak there are small patches of naturally regenerated Norway spruce, Douglas fir, western hemlock and Noble fir along with natural common juniper, beech, oak, holly and a few aspen. The Big Wood lacks an understorey because of the absence of fencing; intense roe deer browsing is very evident.

The great wood-rush (*Luzula sylvatica* Gaud.) covers quite large areas. Its dense mat intercepts rain water, and uses a great deal of soil water, so is inimical to natural regeneration of tree species. Its presence creates a need for screefing or scarification when planting is undertaken. Being a light-demander, the wood-rush disappears following the effective closing of the new crop tree canopy. Also it has been found that wood-rush does not wholly inhibit regeneration of oak if there are plenty of acorns; however, acorns usually fail

to reach the soil and some seedlings may be suppressed by the vegetation. The serious inhibiting factors are the wood-rush sward, infrequency of acorn production and predation by wood-pigeons, etc., insufficient light reaching the forest floor and browsing by roe deer.

In 1984, when further experimenting to achieve a method of converting and perpetuating the oakwood, a 0.4 ha coupe was felled to admit light and fenced against roe deer. A section was rotovated, giving rise to a dense mass of birch and broom seedlings with only few oak interspersed; the remainder, not rotovated, contains a scattering of birch and some good established sapling oak.

The Big Wood of Cawdor is now designated as a Site of Special Scientific Interest. The Nature Conservancy Council's preference was to plan regeneration over a very long period allowing gaps to occur when over-mature specimens blew down. Lord Cawdor, however, felt that such regeneration would be difficult to protect, and that parts of the ageing Big Wood might well succumb before it was adequately regenerated. Subsequently, current negotiations with Scottish National Heritage may favour the group selection system with fencing to help achieve conversion and perpetuation of this ancient oakwood. Although wood-rush hinders natural regeneration, some oak, as well as shade-tolerant conifers, survive; swiping or scarification may increase this. The head forester is Roddy Ross.

Use in Britain: conifers and mixed stands

Research in Scotland on the application of the group selection system to conifers was initiated during the 1950s by Professor M. L. Anderson (see Appendix 5) notably in his work on (a) 'Anderson groups' (Anderson, 1951) and (b) conversions (transformations) from 1953 (Anderson, 1960). He believed that forestry of mixed species and ages when regenerated in small groups would provide and maintain ecological conditions necessary for sustained yield, with some protection from wind and other disturbance factors. This approach seemed especially suitable on higher elevations where diversity would inevitably develop in even-aged plantations through endemic windthrow, disease and site variability. He wished to create some diverse structured forest in Britain and thereby gain experience in its management.

Also in Scotland, Fairbairn (1963), following up Anderson's practical work on groups, clearings or fellings, made a study of wind, aspect, insolation, incident rain and temperature at different points within coniferous groups; and made recommendations for the distribution of planted species within the group. In 1966, McNeill and Thompson (1982) began to monitor the occurrence of Sitka spruce seedlings in the smallest size of clearing (0.04 ha) at Forest of Ae and their survival in relation to their position in the clearings and the vegetation competing with them. Low (1985) reported the occurrence of natural regeneration of Sitka spruce in west and south-west Scotland, but considered that it did not provide a practical alternative to planting because seed years are not regular and the seedbearers are prone to windthrow. During the 1930s and 1950s on frosty sites in Scotland and Wales, use was made of oak and birch as an overwood to establish Douglas fir, western red cedar, Norway spruce and grand fir. Through a period from 1964 to 1970 (Neustein, 1970) studies were made on underplanting for conversion of stands of Scots pine and larches to Douglas fir, western hemlock, grand fir and spruces, using various densities of overwood and strip felling compared with clear cut plots. There exists a considerable amount of unpublished material from Neustein's series of experiments on conversion by underplanting Scots pine and larch in sandy sites and other more fertile sites bearing larch, using Douglas fir, Norway spruce and species of silver fir (Paterson, 1990).

In upland Scotland, five examples of convesion towards group selection in conifers — Glentress Forest, Corrour, Drumlanrig, Faskally and Benevean — are particularly notable.

Glentress Forest lies in the uplands of south-central Scotland. A trial of conversion of 30-year-old conifer stands from uniform even-aged clear cutting system to uneven-aged group selection was begun in 1952. The experimental area was established by an informal agreement between Professor M. L. Anderson, on behalf of the Forestry Department of the University of Edinburgh, and Sir H. Beresford Peirse, Director of the Forestry Commission in Scotland. The aim was to create a mixed forest of irregular structure similar to the beech–spruce–fir protection forests of the Swiss Jura, converting the existing even-aged stands over a period of 60 years.

The total area of the Glentress Trial is 117 ha, the altitudinal range 240-560 m, the annual precipitation 1000-1500 mm, the general aspect south-west, and the windthrow hazard classes 3-4 (exposure to wind is accentuated by funnelling up valleys). At the start of the trial the species were Douglas fir on the lower ground, Japanese and European larch on the middle slopes and Scots pine on the upper slopes; some stands had been partially beaten-up or replaced with Sitka and Norway spruce in the 1940s. There were remnants of old high altitude shelterbelts of European larch and Scots pine; and some 1920 Sitka spruce and Douglas fir below 300 m. Anderson's main objectives were:

- To create mixed stands of diverse structure 'best adapted to the natural conditions' in order to maintain and increase soil fertility.

- To maximise value production by achieving the highest possible volume increment and timber quality.

- To determine the optimum growing stock composition, avoiding the use of extensive clear cutting, for the provision of sustained yield.

- To obtain experience in the management of diverse structure stands.

- To improve internal access to ensure satisfactory harvesting.

Anderson was particularly seeking diverse structure and mixed species, stability to wind, and sustained yield; no apparent emphasis was placed on amenity, landscape, wildlife conservation and sporting/game management. He appears to have underestimated the cost of controlling browse damage (after more than 40 years, some Norway spruce and beech are still below 1 m in height).

The silvicultural system used was group selection: groups of 20 x 10 m or smaller were located on a regular basis with the long axis oriented north-south. Groups in the existing stands were felled and replanted using shade-bearing species at the southern end of each group. Plant spacing was 0.9 m to minimise beating-up and weeding. A total of approximately 2 ha annually were regenerated in the treatment block (total area/conversion period). Species planted initially were Norway spruce, European silver fir, beech, grand fir, western hemlock and broadleaved species including sessile oak, ash, sycamore, alder, hazel, rowan and whitebeam.

The 'check' method of yield control was used: the area was divided into six blocks averaging 19.5 ha each and worked on a 6-year cycle with all operations, including enumeration, done in the year of treatment. Edinburgh University were and are responsible for complete enumerations, for marking thinnings, selecting the regeneration sites, and species. Forest Enterprise undertake harvesting, site preparation, planting, tending and protection. Under recent management (1964 to present) the current objectives are (Whitney McIver *et al.*, 1992):

- To achieve mixed species stands of diverse structure in order to maintain permanent forest conditions throughout the area.

- To achieve sustained production of high quality sawlogs of 40-65 cm dbh, depending on site type.

- To enhance recreation, amenity and conservation values.

- To provide information for education and research relating to the management of diverse structure forest.

From 1964, changes have occurred in silvicultural and management practices. Annual enumerations were discontinued (because the stands were far from achieving a diverse structure) and replaced by periodic sampling (the latest sample enumeration was done in 1991). Group size was increased to reduce shading from the surrounding trees, with larger groups at lower elevations. Groups are made roughly circular with an effective diameter at least twice the surrounding stand height, giving a minimum group size of about 0.1 ha. Choice of species has changed: beech and European silver fir were excluded because of deer browsing; Sitka spruce, Noble fir, western red cedar and hybrid larch were introduced. There will be little further planting of broadleaves because of adequate natural regeneration of sycamore, birch and rowan. The present aim is to establish, over the whole trial, approximately 50% Sitka spruce, 40% other conifers and 10% broadleaved species by area. Natural regeneration of conifer and broadleaved species is occurring on the upper slopes. Several areas of young growth have been respaced to assist in achieving the desired species diversity. Losses from windthrow have been very light. Yield is obtained primarily from the 2 ha annual cut, together with periodic thinning of those stands in mid-rotation. As to economics, it is estimated that establishment costs may be up to 50% higher and harvesting costs 10-20% higher than Forestry Commission standard rates (Shrimpton, 1986, 1988). During conversion there is a cost due to production and revenue foregone; and there is some loss of quality in the edge trees of groups which develop large side branches.

The Glentress Trial is fortunate in being located mainly on freely draining brown earth and ironpan podzol, where windthrow is not a great problem, and in starting with mid-rotation conifers which provide scope for developing diverse structure. Natural regeneration has been helpful, and is now tending to replace planting on all sites except those with dense soft grasses (*Holcus*) on moist gley soils. The early experience of sheep grazing and deer browsing emphasises that strict control of these animals is fundamental to such group selection working. Only after about half the conversion period does the diverse structure become apparent (Fairbairn, 1963; Blyth 1986; Blyth and Malcolm, 1988; Shrimpton, 1986, 1988; Whitney McIver, 1991; Whitney McIver *et al.*, 1992; Malcolm, 1992).

The Glentress Trial is an excellent education resource; it has provided a wide range of research topics. Other benefits are the high standard of amenity, nature conservation and forest recreation values (Plate 11). In managing this important trial, the Forestry Department of the University of Edinburgh — particularly in recent years through Douglas Malcolm, John Blyth and Helen Whitney McIver — has played a leading role in demonstrating conversion to diverse structure forestry in Scotland.

Corrour Forest, Inverness-shire

Corrour Forest lies in wet uplands in the West Highlands of Scotland. Sir John Stirling Maxwell began the afforestation in 1892 using Scots pine; but planting of mixed west North American conifers followed (Anderson, 1967). The forest lies at 380 to 460 m; the moorland soils over granite are of low to moderate fertility. M. L. Anderson in 1952 began a trial of conversion to group selection forest, using the *Méthode du Contrôle* or 'Check' Method to determine increment and control yield. The trial was located on the better soils south of Loch Ossian.

The main object was to create a balanced growing stock of exotic species capable of continuous production. Recurrent inventories began in 1952 and the area to be included in the trial was finalised in 1958 as 54 ha in six blocks. In 1958 the species composing the stands were Norway and Sitka spruce (73%), grand and noble firs (7%) and the remainder Scots pine, European larch, birch and other broadleaves. Much of the initial variance in

structure was associated with change of species, checked growth and site quality. Each year one block was completely enumerated and trees were marked for felling. The equivalent of heavy crown thinnings was made to break up the stands into groups of different diameter classes and all these fellings were completed by the end of the second cycle of inventory in 1964.

In 1965 the Forestry Commission acquired the woodlands, the enumerations continued and the third cycle was completed, so that data from 19 years were available. Malcolm (1971) reported that the current annual increment of the trial was 10.7 m^3 ha^{-1}, so that a mean annual increment of 7.1 m^3 ha^{-1} could be assumed; this was reasonable for a high elevation site. When fully converted, the trial forest was expected to yield about 45 m^3 ha^{-1} at each felling on a 6-year cycle. Trees of about 50 cm diameter at breast height were expected in 80 years. Regeneration of Sitka spruce was appearing and the size of clearings was 0.04 to 0.2 ha, with the larger sizes preferred.

This example of conversion to group selection system would have had particular relevance to the type of stand structure which may be necessary for the protection of forest fringes at higher elevation. Unfortunately, work on the groups ceased owing to changes of ownership and distance from research centres (Paterson, 1990). The groups suffered from inadequate fencing against deer. A diverse stand structure had been initiated in compartment 3 (Plate 12). In 1983, following the State's disposal, much of the mature timber was clear felled. Some replanting took place but the trial terminated as far as inventory control is concerned. The present owner is Donald Maxwell Macdonald and the forest manager is Felix Karthaus.

Drumlanrig, near Thornhill, Dumfriesshire

Drumlanrig, the estate of His Grace the Duke of Buccleuch, has examples of group selection in Bogrie Wood and Mallyford extending to some 173 ha on rising ground and important to the landscape setting of the Castle. The woodland manager is Bob Jordan.

Between the years 1900 and 1949, sporadic planting into old broadleaved and mixed stands extended to some 11 ha, mainly of European larch, hybrid larch, Norway spruce and Douglas fir. Between 1953 and 1973 group felling and replanting took place annually, totalling 108 ha, the main species being Japanese larch, Norway spruce, Sitka spruce and Douglas fir, 'with small quantities of Scots pine, European larch, western hemlock, oak and beech. In the early part of this period the coupes were small, following M. L. Anderson's recommendations but later coupes were larger, up to 0.5 ha each. Where large broadleaves, Scots pine or Wellingtonia stood in the coupe area they were retained. These plantings are now overdue for thinning but do present marketing problems due to the diversity of species and size class, giving only small quantities of any one product.

Planting during the period 1974 to 1992 amounted to some 17 ha in the three years 1977, 1979 and 1988, using only Scots pine and Sitka spruce. Current policy is to replant following windthrow rather than create new coupes on a planned basis. Browsing by deer is the main disincentive to fully pursuing the group selection system.

Drumlanrig illustrates the value of group selection in a sensitive landscape. It also highlights continuity of management, felling and relief thinning around groups, replanting and appropriate sized coupes as vital for success; but overriding these factors is the need for practical and economic control of browsing and bark-stripping mammals.

These woods are commercial and are worked within the whole management plan of the estate. Elsewhere, the planned rotation is 60 years for the even-aged clear fell and replant system but in the Drumlanrig policy woods a diverse scene was quickly created through the use of the group selection system, to be improved in age and species over a longer period. Throughout the estate, this type of treatment is to be continued where there are even-aged areas which were originally planted for shelter, amenity and sporting, and therefore will require to be regenerated on a group selection system aiming for continuous forest cover.

Faskally Wood, Perthshire

North-west of Pitlochry, Faskally Wood, consisting of mixed conifers and broadleaves, was originally planted as policy woods for a Victorian mansion, now Faskally House. The soils are mainly freely drained fertile morainic. In 1947 the estate was purchased by the North of Scotland Hydro-Electric Board; and for several years the House was used as a staff college, and Faskally Wood formed part of a public relations campaign to convince the public that the Board was sensitive to environmental concerns (Newton, 1986).

In 1953 the Forestry Commission acquired ownership, under the proviso that no clear cutting would occur. From 1955 until 1969-70, Faskally House was the site of one of the Foresters' Training Schools. The management of Faskally Wood from 1953 was within a plan designed by M. L. Anderson of the Department of Forestry, University of Edinburgh. With the co-operation of Frank Oliver of the Forestry Commission's Aberdeen office, he planned a group selection system in the long term and suggested detailed prescriptions for the conversion. The group sizes ranged from 0.02-0.05 ha, later increased to 0.05-0.10 ha, the whole to be converted over a 120-year period.

Anderson recommended in 1953 that about 75 ha for 'irregular working' should be subdivided into blocks on a 6-year cycle, one block to be dealt with each year. Groups in general were to be 'dispersed over each compartment'. Where natural regeneration was hoped for but did not appear in 3 years, planting was to be undertaken; birch regeneration was to be made use of for nursing. Two years later, in 1955, Anderson confirmed to H. Cruickshank in charge of the School that the intention was that the groups of small stands among large blocks of even-aged Scots pine, larch, Douglas fir and Norway spruce should consist of shade-bearers and semi-shade-bearers; that 'it would be a mistake to make the openings and groups too large'; and that 'a small proportion of larch and Scots pine may be desirable and a good deal of oak [in the oak stands] which may require larger openings'. No group should be less than 0.02-0.05 ha. Anything that would make Faskally Wood more uniform should be avoided. The system of group selection in mixed conifers and broadleaves, primarily for amenity and recreation as well as for continuous forest cover, was applied sensitively to the environment.

Today after 40 years the original 'Anderson groups' are sometimes difficult to recognise. They have become tall, cramped and require relief by thinning; and in general have proved to be too small and too detailed in species layout. However, they are growing well and will be improved by thinning and freeing of their edges. They still enhance the interest and productivity of Faskally Wood, and diversify the structure (Plate 13). A detailed stand inventory was made in each working block in turn by the staff and students of the Forestry School, but ceased when it closed.

In 1971 Faskally House was bought by Glasgow Corporation, and in 1973 opened as a Schools' Outdoor Centre. In the 1970s Faskally Wood was incorporated in the Forestry Commission's Tummel Forest administration. It was the first wood in East Scotland Conservancy to have timber production ranked lower in objectives than recreation and diversity for internal landscaping of high quality. In 1977 a new management plan was prepared for the period 1977-86, emphasising four objectives:

1. To provide and enhance the structure and species diversity of the area, creating a recreational wood of high amenity.

2. To provide adequate essential visitor facilities to meet present and future recreational demand.

3. To conserve the environment in Faskally Wood primarily as a means of enhancing its amenity value and visitor enjoyment.

4. To provide high quality timber as efficiently as the above-mentioned objectives permit.

Disposals have reduced the net management area of Faskally Wood to about 51 ha. The plan was only partially followed and little new planting undertaken. In 1987 a new Forestry Commission plan was formulated and adopted. Recommended group size was 0.05-0.50 ha; abundant regeneration of Douglas fir, sycamore and beech was available; the dominant species included Scots pine, European larch, Douglas fir, oak, birch and beech. A proportion of the older trees were felled as mature and a proportion of younger trees are removed periodically. Replanting has been of small areas where there is insufficient natural regeneration. Today, there are about 23 different species of trees, a pleasing mosaic of conifers and broadleaves with a great variety of ages and sizes including many fine examples of Douglas fir and silver firs, some over 100 years old, and wild cherry, oak, birch, rowan, lime, elm, ash, sycamore, beech, alder and poplar. The whole is a splendid area for amenity and recreation, sensitively managed to complement timber production. Current Forest Enterprise intentions for the Wood are:

- To continue to sensitively manage for amenity and recreation purposes, including semi-permanent or continuous forest cover.

- To thin the 'Anderson groups' (horse extraction may be used).

- To create some additional regeneration groups.

- To sensitively remove by selection some of the fine mature Scots pine and larch.

Owned by the Forestry Commission, Benevean Wood in Glen Affric is an example of group or random regeneration of indigenous Scots pine (Plate 14). Stands had arisen from extensive natural regeneration following exploitation of all mid-sized and large trees of good quality around 1770. An area of about 850 ha was brought into a ring deer fence in 1959-60 and later subdivided into three sections to improve deer control. An annual programme of about 12 ha in six separate felled 2 ha groups was initiated from 1960 on the premise that mean age was already 140-180 years and few trees could be expected to remain healthy beyond another 70 years. Therefore, the regeneration period envisaged was 70 years. Many trees were already thin in the crown and being killed by *Trametes pini* crown and stem rot and *Stereum* butt rot. The 2 ha groups were centred on the more open sickly parts of these old stands. Artificial ground preparation was used: normally turfing in deep *Sphagnum*; ploughing was attempted but *Calluna* and mosses fouled the ploughs. Later, Affric Scots pine seed was collected and plants from this seed were used. In fact, a lot of regeneration emerged generally from the *Calluna* after improved protection from red deer. This group felling was continued for only 5 to 10 years. Thereafter, random regeneration was accepted although it appears to be less dependable where there is no extraction skidding in harvesting to expose a seedbed. Occasional windthrow is presenting new openings and soil disturbance for regeneration.

In upland Wales, the two examples chosen of conversion of conifer plantations to group selection are: Cefn Llwyd Forest and Coed y Brenin. Two further examples (not described here) are Diosgydd (Plate 15) and Nant BH (Plate 16), both in Gwynedd.

Situated south-east of Bala, the 439 ha Cefn Llywd Forest has been owned since 1986 by Shotton Paper Company plc and managed by Talis Kalnars. (The Forest Manager since January 1993 is Philippe Morgan.) It is mainly of uniform even-aged conifer planted in 1952-63 with 100 ha in 1988-91. The site types are 247 ha upland with peaty gleys and ironpan soils, 147 ha lowland (brown earth). The basic geology is Silurian and the annual rainfall 1500 mm. The main species is Sitka spruce (63%) with some Douglas fir, larch and Scots pine, and about 1% broadleaves. The management aims are:

1. To maximise the return on the financial investment by the production of the highest volume of quality timber.

2. To convert from uniform even-aged plantation to uneven-aged mixed species forest.

3. To *normalise* production, cash flow, and aesthetic and environmental benefits by the practice of sustainable forestry and achievement of continuous forest cover.

Since 1986 all compartments have been thinned on a graduated density pattern that aims to increase production of high quality timber and to introduce irregularity into stands. The larger part of the Forest is managed under a progressive small coupe felling as part of the 20-year restructure plan begun in 1993. The remainder is managed under other more specialised systems, each with a degree of irregularity. The progressive small clear cuts will be limited to 0.5-1.0 ha, opened on windfirm edges, and advancing progressively towards the prevailing wind. Topographical variation and physical division by tracks and roads allow felling of coupes to start from numerous points to accommodate the annual cut determined by the length of the conversion period which itself is constrained by top height and windthrow risk. Small coupes maintain the forest environment and assist in the management of natural regeneration, which is the preferred means of restocking. Planting or direct seeding after cultivation are options where regeneration fails or is constrained by the terms of the field sporting agreement.

Site type and species productivity determine the choice of species. A particular aim is to increase the area under Douglas fir in the lower sites. With natural regeneration, species choice and composition is made during respacing to about 2 m x 2 m, when seedlings are about 1 m tall. Choice and proportion are varied to suit site requirements, silvicultural system employed, amenity, and water guidelines. An element of broadleaves will be included to satisfy conditions of the Woodland Grant Scheme. Current species composition is typically Sitka spruce (90%), Japanese larch, Scots pine and broadleaves (10%).

Some compartments are managed under a variety of irregular systems that have been chosen to suit site requirements and amenity. They are single tree, group selection, strip and irregular shelterwood systems. The system combines features of different systems and is best described as 'a strip and group system'. Felling is done on a strip of width twice top height. Use is made of advance regeneration (typically Sitka spruce, Japanese larch, Scots pine, birch and rowan). The aim in these high production areas is a species mix of Sitka spruce, Japanese larch, Scots pine and broadleaves. Strips are felled progressively against the prevailing wind, either on a 6-year cycle or when natural regeneration enters the thicket stage. Thinning will take place in adjacent strips; 80% of the new strip will be retained as groups and shelterwood and the retained portion of the previously felled strip removed, providing access through the regeneration. A portion of the original retained areas may be reserved at each stage depending on the constraints of windthrow or the requirements of yield control and markets.

One compartment is managed under a single tree or group selection system. Two preparatory thinning operations were done in which selection was across the dbh range and not to favour large trees. A minimum exploitable diameter of 42 cm is set so that only trees that have reached their exploitable diameter are selectively felled creating gaps in which regeneration is accepted. Where two or more adjacent trees are felled together, the system tends towards group selection and allows retention of light-demanding species.

The aim of conversion is to achieve *normality*. Several restructuring phases will be required to achieve this. The first plan spans 20 years. A second plan (again first rotation) will restructure the recently planted areas. Further restructuring will be required beyond this point before the Forest produces sustainable supplies of timber and non-wood benefits.

Continuous production will help to ensure sustained supplies of logs for sawmilling, and smaller produce for pulpwood, chipboard and fencing. The Forest as a whole will be mixed in species. The stands managed under the small coupe felling system will be generally even-aged. Stands managed under the more irregular systems will have a greater range of age classes with a tendency to *normalise* within compartments. The effect will be virtually continuous forest cover.

Coed y Brenin, North Wales

Coed y Brenin lies within Forest Enterprise's Dolgellau Forest District (c. 17 000 ha) in North Wales. Site conditions are generally very favourable: highly productive brown earths on sheltered sites dominate the mid and lower slopes. Gradual introduction of alternative silvicultural systems is being made to some sites throughout the District. Something approaching 1% might be suitable for conversion during the next decade. Much consideration is being given to achieving some biological diversity. The aim is to achieve both structural and species diversity, mainly by the group selection system, paying special regard to aesthetic and environmental benefits, and matching species to site conditions. At the same time, timber production is to be sustained. An important principle to be followed is what is considered best for the future of the Forest and the set objectives, not least achieving environmental objectives, as well as meeting timber production requirements. Appropriate thought is given as to the opportunity cost of conversion (T. Owen, personal communication).

Particular experiments and actions are aimed at the achievement of virtually continuous forest cover by (a) converting some uniform, even-aged mid-rotation or maturing conifers into uneven-aged diverse structure by the group selection system, and (b) recruiting natural regeneration into maturing or mature high quality conifer stands (especially Douglas fir and Japanese larch which will have extended rotation age) in areas requiring sensitive management for reasons of landscape, amenity, wildlife habitat and recreational potential. At the same time, timber production will meet set objectives.

Achievement of the foregoing will be sought mainly by manipulation of conifer stands by careful selective removal of individual large stems (significantly Douglas fir) or by felling small coupes (0.1 to 0.2 ha), restocking if possible by natural regeneration or by planting, or, experimentally, by new methods of direct seeding. Another aim is to perpetuate part of the forest cover by changing the thinning regime to retain mixed size classes, including small stems. Wide choices are intended, all expected to be of help in future management.

Additionally in Wales, there are two notable examples of diverse structure forestry, in part using variants of group selection and uniform shelterwood.

Ffrwdgrech Woodlands, South Wales

Owned by Major W. D. D. Evans, the Ffrwdgrech Woodlands near Brecon comprise a fine example of continuous forest cover extending over the last 30 years. Ninety hectares of well-stocked woodlands, managed by Talis Kalnars, contain a wide variety of both conifer (80%) and broadleaved species (20%), the preferred species being Douglas fir and ash. They are run on the group selection system with continuous cover being maintained, as far as possible, by the annual use of group fellings and selection fellings followed by planting. The harvesting is largely oriented to exploitable diameter and is not related to age. There are regular checks, using callipers and counters, every 5 years, to assess the growing stock, thereby monitoring the production levels, the profitability, and the gradual increase in standing volume and value. The woodlands are of high amenity value. The group selection areas as well as natural regeneration are particularly impressive. Wildlife habitats are being improved as well as soil structure and fertility.

Clocaenog, North-east Wales

The main block lies within Forest Enterprise's Clwyd Forest District (c. 9250 ha). Soil conditions on the wet and exposed Hiraethog plateau tend to favour Sitka spruce, although larch and Norway spruce grow on the lower southern levels. In recent years as clear cutting of the older spruce has evolved, opportunities have arisen to plan the second generation woodlands. This planning takes account of environmental principles, embracing landscape, conservation, water, public access and recreation, and reinforces the concept of multi-purpose forestry (P. Hughes, personal communication).

Natural regeneration of Sitka spruce is prolific on most clear fell sites in Clocaenog, and it will be the main species in the restocking process. Larch and pine also regenerate on some areas, and by careful management, an acceptable mixture of conifer species can be achieved. Further diversification is realised by the introduction of broadleaved species on all sites. Even on those areas where Sitka spruce regeneration dominates, it is possible to find space and the opportunity to plant larch, Norway spruce and pine. Some long-term retention, the combination of overstorey with an understorey crop, also contribute to the diverse structure of the forest block.

Producing and maintaining a programmed supply of timber is one of the main objectives and the main source of revenue. Clear fell coupes are planned to achieve this programme but the process is arranged so that restocked crops reach heights of 2 m or more before an adjacent coupe is felled. This in itself ensures sound diversity, and in conjunction with the species mixture results in the gradual change from even-aged stands to forest of mixed age and species.

In the lowlands of England, adaptations or variants of group selection in conifers are demonstrated in the following three examples, two in Devon, one in Wiltshire.

Dartington, Devon

W. E. Hiley in 1943 tried a version of the group selection system (Hiley, 1953, 1964, 1967). In a stand of Douglas fir, Japanese larch, Norway spruce and Sitka spruce of varied ages from 22 to 46 years, gaps were created by heavy thinning to 370 stems ha^{-1}, and planted with groups of Douglas fir, Japanese larch and sweet chestnut. During the 1950s, further group planting took place, mainly of Douglas fir and western red cedar. Hiley was particularly pleased with the good growth shown by the isolated overstorey trees, and there was very little wind damage. However, by the early 1960s he appeared to have rejected any further application of the system on silvicultural and management grounds (Howell et al., 1983). Although he considered that enough had been done to show that Douglas fir and Japanese larch could be grown under a form of group selection, he felt that natural regeneration could not be relied upon because

of rampant weed growth (particularly bramble) which smothered the seedlings, and that the small size of the groups would make their tending and thinning too expensive.

Hiley had used the *Méthode du Contrôle* (Hiley, 1967), considering this to be the most practicable, if rather laborious, means of regulating yield. It required intensive measurement and management and took much time to achieve reasonable accuracy since it involved the periodic measurement (say every 5 or 10 years) of all the trees above a certain minimum size. By a comparison of the results of a progression of periodic measurements called recurrent inventory, it is possible to achieve reliable estimates of the growing stock volume, the distribution of size classes, the increment and hence the periodic cut of timber and its distribution among the size classes and species (Paterson, 1958; Howell et al., 1983).

In spite of Hiley's rejection of his system, a part of compartments 1 and 2 at North Wood, which includes his original sample plot, has continued to be treated in a way consistent with group selection principles. As a result, this is a particularly attractive part of the woodlands, much frequented by the public. Subsequently, it was decided to maintain the character of this area with an attempt to operate the system (Howell et al., 1983). The original experimental plot withstood the gales of 1989-90 whereas an even-aged stand of coast redwood nearby was flattened. The main problems Hiley foresaw in applying the system concerned economics, extraction costs, and the possible difficulties in using it to grow his most profitable species, Douglas fir and Japanese larch, because of their limited shade tolerance after early youth.

Longleat, Wiltshire

This example is on the estate of Lord Bath, on freely drained podzolised brown earth derived from Greensand with light weed growth on low ridges. John McHardy, the forest manager, has applied to conifers a shelterwood-cum-group selection system with evolving stand structure on some 300 ha (Hart, 1991). It is, in fact, conversion to groups from even-aged plantations of Scots pine, Douglas fir and larch. A 10-year treatment cycle is used, and stands are kept very open to accommodate such light-demanding species as larch and pines (Plate 17). The system has partly arisen as a side-product of the very heavy crown thinnings applied to all the 20 to 30-year-old larch, Scots pine and Douglas fir plantations. These thinnings have encouraged development of fairly plentiful natural regeneration of those species which are focused into groups by group fellings. The regeneration is respaced with a clearing saw when 1.5-2 m in height. Apart from applications of 'Asulox' to control bracken every few years in the regeneration groups, this is the only tending undertaken. The aim is to establish and respace a new crop of regeneration every decade, although fellings or thinnings of the overstorey are generally every 5 years. Stocking in the older stands at present is light and there is some sacrifice of volume production; however, as more age or size classes become established, canopy should become more complete, and weed growth reduced. The low stocking compared with Continental selection stands means that high pruning is necessary on final stand trees but diameter increment is outstandingly high, and the expected age of exploitation is 40-50 years.

Tavistock Woodland Estate, South Devon

The Bradford-Hutt Plan pursued on the Tavistock Woodland Estate has been the most intensive organised conversion to the group selection system recently evolved and practised in Britain (Hutt and Watkins, 1971; Hart, 1991). In brief, each stand is divided geometrically into square 'units' (18 m x 18 m) and each of these units is further divided into nine square 'plots' measuring 6 m x 6 m. Plots are intended to contain one final stand tree, and are initially planted with nine shade-bearing transplants consisting of conifers apart from a few *Nothofagus* species. The existing stand within a unit is felled and replanted at 6-year intervals, so each unit eventually will contain plots of all ages. The uneven-aged units taken together as a stand are considered as the basic group, and the Plan qualifies as a group selection system. The continuous canopy is particularly important. Part of the Tavistock Woodland Estate has recently been sold and management is now fragmented but continuation of the Plan, which is half completed, is likely.

Conclusions on the group selection system

The conditions of climate, site and vegetation being remarkably varied in Britain, it is not surprising that experience gained from the use of the group selection system has also been varied. Sometimes it has been difficult to classify the examples because distinctions between variants and adaptations of systems have become blurred. But it is important to use recognisable labels to establish norms. Nevertheless, individual stands studied for this Bulletin, together with many relevant discussions with their managers, reveal much common ground and this is now identified.

1. *The objectives of conversion.* As might be expected, almost every owner or forester gave the production and sustained yield of timber as the prime aim but several emphasised quality of timber, especially in broadleaves, in addition to quantity of timber. The statements of other objectives usually gave as important the creation of continuous forest cover; diversity in species, age and canopy structure; amenity; improved habitat for wildlife; facilities for field sports; and access for recreation, the emphasis given varying with circumstances.

2. *Choice of sites*. It is notable (see Table 3.3) that most owners and their foresters have played safe and selected relatively sheltered sites in favourable wind zones (Quine and White, 1993) which should allow the stands to have a low risk of strong gales, but does not rule out endemic wind damage; the sites usually have soils that can be penetrated by tree roots to a good depth. Soils that are wet and cannot be deeply rooted have been avoided and the deeper fertile loams — brown earths, soils with sandy texture and podzols — have been preferred. Natural regeneration is often easier to obtain on such soils. The techniques commonly used in the group selection system have not been tested on more exposed sites, with the possible exceptions of Dartington in Devon and Corrour Forest in Inverness-shire.

3. *Species*. Existing broadleaved species to be continued in the converted wood or forest include oak, ash, wild cherry, sycamore, lime and beech; and Scots pine, larches, Douglas fir, Norway spruce and Sitka spruce among conifers. Species that have been introduced in the course of conversion are often shade-tolerant conifers including grand fir, Noble fir, western hemlock and western red cedar. Beech has proved difficult to introduce in conifer forest owing to deer browse.

4. *Age of stand at the start of conversion*. Conversion has followed two main routes. Either 'derelict woodland' of varying age and condition has been cleared of poor quality stems, while stands and trees of good growth and quality have been favoured, tended and augmented; or clearings have been made in existing productive stands and regenerated naturally or by planting. The former route is common in broadleaved stands, while the latter route has been followed in both broadleaved and conifer stands. When existing productive stands are to be converted, the process has begun at all ages from 30 to 100 years or even more. However, most foresters agree that conversion should begin earlier (at 30 to 50 years) rather than later (at 80 years or more). A common stimulus to conversion has been the appearance of natural regeneration following heavy thinnings. Areas of 'advance growth' are encouraged to expand by further removals of the overstorey, and this is systematised into a plan for group selection.

5. *Silvicultural prescriptions*. When the starting point has been selectively exploited woodland or 'derelict' woodland, the bare land not already stocked with trees has been regenerated by planting groups of one or sometimes two species. When the starting point has been maturing, mature or over-mature woodland, 'advance growth' has been augmented by planting with the same or different species. Experience suggests that it is a mistake to use several species in underplanted groups or to plant them too densely (normal planting distances are adequate). However, 'advance growth' cannot always be expected to recover when light is admitted by thinning and felling the overstorey which is sometimes the case with beech. Much depends on species and the condition of the regeneration at time of release.

6. *Size of group*. Almost all owners and foresters contacted for this Bulletin began with small groups of less than 0.2 ha but as they gained experience the size of group used has enlarged. Some consider that Britain's summers are more cloudy than those common on the Continent so there is less light at ground level; others wish to retain light-demanding species in the new crop; others again wish to ensure that the groups created will survive without excessive treatment of the overstorey and surround. Typical sizes of groups are now 0.3 to 1.0 ha, which can be treated as units for tending, harvesting and yield control (see Tables 3.1 and 3.2).

In all group adaptations, the size of groups, their shape, orientation, distribution and protection have been critical elements in prescriptions; size is particularly important. Natural regeneration of large-seeded species (notably oak and beech) may not spread to the centre of large groups. On the other hand, Brown (1953) commented on the 'pudding-shaped profile' of beech frequently found in groups, with taller regeneration in the centre of the group; this is typical of groups that are too small or have not been enlarged when regeneration has appeared. Larger groups are needed in taller and more uneven-aged stands as well as for full and partial light-demanders. The limitations imposed by natural regeneration do not apply in the same degree where planting is used to augment the stocking, and this will normally be the case in most situations.

Scrutiny of European literature and discussions with foresters in Britain on group cuttings reveals wide divergence of opinion about suitable dimensions. The size of clearings depends largely on features of the climate, soil, final tree height at harvesting, and species. Suitable dimensions must be worked out for each location using experience gained elsewhere as a starting point. One working rule emerging from the range of opinion is that the first sizes of clearings chosen are commonly too small and must often be doubled usually by thinning the overstorey (Matthews, 1986). Table 3.1 is intended as a guide to assessing possible sizes of clearings sufficient to provide growing space for final crop trees of Douglas fir (Hutt and Watkins, 1971; Bradford, 1981), ash and sycamore (Garfitt, 1984) and oak (Jobling and Pearce, 1977).

Matthews (1986, 1989) gives a table of 'dimensions of clearings to provide growing space for trees of final size' (see Table 3.2). Groups in broadleaves need to be larger for ash, oak and sycamore than for beech owing to their different light requirements. In view of the foregoing information, after considering wind effect and deer browsing probabilities, groups should be used that are as large as the site conditions and species requirements will allow but generally will be less than 1 ha to maximise the benefits of natural regeneration and side shelter and protection from excessive insolation.

7. *Access and extraction.* There is sparse information about access for tending, but some owners and foresters emphasise that tending and extraction paths must be integrated with the spatial arrangement of groups.

Because the group selection forest develops as a mosaic of groups of different species, ages and canopies, some planned skeleton layout of extraction routes is desirable. Much depends on the existing road system and how it is to be used.

8. *The treatment cycle.* Continental foresters consider that a cycle of 6 years is about right, so they have divided the whole area to be treated by the group selection system into six roughly equal 'blocks' or areas. Each block is treated at intervals of 6 years, cleaning and respacing stands that have reached the thicket stage, thinning, occasionally high pruning, and clear felling followed by regeneration. One forester would emphasise the importance of thorough cleaning of young stands, another would recommend delaying cleaning until first thinning, and yet another would prefer selection and favouring of the best saplings only, a form of respacing. There seems to be ample room for inventiveness on the part of foresters. The areas being treated by the group selection system range from 6 to 300 ha, with many less than 100 ha. In Britain a large proportion of private woodlands fall within the range of 50 to 100 ha and it seems probable that the group selection system will suit this extent, where sites are suitable.

9. *Protection.* Foresters are adamant that deer, rabbits and grey squirrels must be controlled in numbers. Some have used temporary internal fencing to protect regeneration, but rarely are treeshelters used for this purpose. If group selection is to become more widespread, rangers and gamekeepers are likely to be in good demand and field sporting may need to be encouraged.

10. *Vegetation control.* An interesting feature is provided by the reference to the barriers to regeneration caused by particular plant species, e.g. the great wood-rush at Cawdor and *Holcus* and grass swards generally, and predation by small mammals such as mice and voles. Generally it is essential to control vegetation by herbicides or mulches

or manipulation of the overstorey, or by use of an understorey.

11. *Management.* A rotation for group selection is rarely specified, because a fine tree is allowed to grow on until the value increment ceases. If this practice became general, it could be a good advertisement for forestry. Precise costs and benefits are also lacking, partly because mixed, uneven-aged and irregular stands have so far been a small part of British forestry and no values have been placed on high amenity in economic appraisal. There is need for inventory and periodic measurement of development of the desired structure (see Appendix 3).

12. *Factors causing difficulty.* Continuity of management is essential and, if it falters, several unfortunate things happen. The most obvious is that groups of young regeneration begin to run short of light and need relief by thinning of the upper storey or cleaning within the groups. Again, if thinnings are delayed, the older trees dominate and trees of the lower size classes soon suffer. A possible useful guide is that there must not be weakly co-dominants and sub-dominants in the stand; the trees must thrive and make their contribution to the whole canopy. A forester used to thinning a uniform stand from below must instead thin from above and concentrate on the crowns and the canopies. Use of groups that are too small in area is a common problem. No forester wishes to open the canopy unduly and admit wind, so the group selection system must normally be restricted to windthrow hazard class 1-3, and to deep soils that permit good root development. Typically, one or two tree species will dominate the stand and site, making it difficult to keep others in a mixed group. To adequately satisfy the needs of two species is sometimes difficult; to meet the needs of more than three is full of problems.

13. *Factors leading to success.* Besides continuity of management, sustained ownership by enthusiastic and patient practitioners is essential; so too is staff training to impart the skills of conversion and management. The period of conversion for conifers must not exceed 30 to 40 years, which is roughly equal to the working lives of two foresters. It is likely that three principal species which are compatible with each other in their light requirements are sufficient; any others should be secondary and occupy the lower canopies. Any suggestion that a group selection stand constructed by patient care and attention is 'self-perpetuating' must be forgotten, although readiness to intervene and experiment to gain experience will do much to ease what is obviously a satisfying task.

Chapter 4

The single tree selection system

Introduction

In the single tree selection system, felling and regeneration are distributed over the whole management area. The fellings are called selection fellings; they remove single trees and are combined with thinning among the various size classes, and aim to perpetuate a structure in which all age and size classes are mixed together over every part of the stand. Unlike the clear cutting or shelterwood systems, the single tree selection system maintains a continuous forest cover: viewed from both without and within, the scene and the environment appear stable and unchanging. The fellings and thinnings create quite small gaps to be regenerated by natural seeding, and on the Continent the species are virtually all moderately or very shade-tolerant, e.g. European silver fir, Norway spruce and beech.

Application on the Continent

The system is commonly used in Europe where important management objectives are site protection and enhancement of the external landscape. It is often advocated as 'natural' and 'perpetual' forest. Stands managed under single tree selection are protective in several senses: continuous forest cover protects the soil; frost-sensitive species such as beech are sheltered; and the lack of sharp edges to the canopy plus the strong taper of the tree stems, generally give increased firmness against wind and snow. Another important attribute is its help in regulating water flow into catchments.

The single tree selection system as applied in central Europe is the classic example of con-

tinuous forest cover. It involves regular removal of single trees of marketable size within the dominants, distributed throughout the stand and adjustment of stem-size class numbers to conform with a stem-number curve. A system of extraction paths aids harvesting and reduces damage to regeneration. However, when experienced staff and directional felling are employed, damage is much less than might be expected. Where conditions are favourable, natural regeneration springs up in the small gaps created by the felled trees. Measures to assist regeneration may include removal of excess raw humus, soil cultivation and even planting in gaps caused by felling or accident. Under ideal conditions, this process goes on year after year throughout the whole stand, resulting in the constant maintenance over the whole management area of the uneven-aged structure in which trees of all sizes are mixed together in numbers conforming to the ideal stem-number curve (age is not recognised, just as rotation is not). Such perfect distribution is seldom actually found, the small size classes occurring more usually in patches resulting from regeneration springing up in small gaps. Thinnings among the various size classes are necessary to provide for sustained yield and quality, ensuring that:

- the various classes are maintained in their correct proportions;
- a suitable mixture of species (where required) is maintained;
- young growth is freed from suppression.

Cleanings are also undertaken among the younger age classes.

The selection and felling of single trees scattered over the whole management area would be impracticable except in stands of small size, and hence, on the Continent, this procedure (sometimes called the 'ideal' selection system) is usually confined to woods or small forests belonging to private individuals or communities. In forests of larger size, it is customary to divide the area into several more or less equal 'blocks', in one of which selection fellings are made each year, so that the whole forest is worked over during a period of years ('the felling cycle' is equal to the number of blocks). Under this 'periodic' selection system, fellings are more concentrated, there being an accumulation of mature trees during the interval between two successive interventions in the same 'block', so that a larger volume per hectare is available than in the case of annual fellings extending over the whole forest. The felling cycle is fixed according to the circumstances of each case. It is generally not more than 10 years and is often less; in France, usually between 5 and 8 years, rarely more than 8 years; and in Switzerland 6 to 10 years. In most instances the periodic yield is relatively diverse in size classes and may be more difficult to market.

In Switzerland, the regulation of the yield of timber from selection forests is by the *Méthode du Contrôle* or 'Check' Method devised by the French forester Biolley (1920) and described in detail by Knüchel (1953) and in outline by Anderson (1953), Paterson (1958) and Osmaston (1968). Biolley adopted the principle of gaining maximum volume increment from the smallest possible growing stock, and set out to maintain a definite distribution of size classes so as to establish a *normal* forest and ensure sustained yields. He divided the forest into compartments and made recurrent inventories of the growing stock in three size classes (large, medium and small) at intervals of 6 to 10 years, to determine the relation between increment and growing stock, fix the yield for the next period and plan the fellings and thinnings to work towards the *normal* distribution of size classes. It is difficult to appreciate the significance of the full control system in Britain, where most woods are in a far from *normal* state (Hart, 1991). However, stem-number curves are a simple and easy to use guideline (Philip, 1994).

Advantages of the single tree selection system are: by maintaining a continuous forest cover, exposure of the soil is reduced and protection provided against erosion, landslips and avalanches; and damage by wind and snow is minimised. All seed years can yield regeneration, however infrequent or partial, and the seedlings are protected. It is possible to promote the development of individual trees with good form and branching habit and to retain them as long as they are making valuable increment because the crowns of the dominant trees are long and well-developed and stand more or less isolated. The lower parts of the stems of trees of large size yield timber of high quality but the upper exposed parts do produce large knots, and taper markedly.

Selection forest, aesthetically and environmentally, is usually very attractive, bringing benefits to the owner and the general public. A further advantage sometimes argued is that the system is 'natural', resembling natural indigenous forest. This is not widely accepted. Peterken (1981) and Peterken *et al.* (1992) assert that such stands are unnatural, being the product of sustained, skilled and highly regulated forestry working with a small group of shade-tolerant species. The system is particularly well suited to small woods or forests where intensive working and close supervision are possible.

Disadvantages of the single tree selection system are that it is one of the most intensive, needing considerable silvicultural skill, continuity in management and ownership, and care in marking, felling and extraction. The system is applicable chiefly to shade-tolerant species on well-drained soils, and is unsuitable for areas where windthrow risk is high. The work of tending, felling and extraction is scattered and on a small scale, needing experienced and knowledgeable supervision, and the costs are likely to be higher than those in a comparable area of even-aged forest. Control of browsing and bark-stripping mammals is probably more difficult than in even-aged forest, hence damage done can be more severe.

The single tree selection system is important in the mountainous regions of Europe, especially in Switzerland where it must be practised by legislation for protection purposes; examples are the mixed conifer and broadleaved selection forests of the Vosges, Jura, Alps and Carpathians. Often the main purpose is to divert snow avalanches and rock slides away from villages. The main species are Norway spruce, European silver fir and beech, with some sycamore, rowan, lime and occasional other species. The beech is used to maintain fertility of the soil and depress weed growth. There are several variants of the main forest type and all are typically montane, being confined to hills and the middle slopes of the mountains and rising to elevations of 1500 m where the geology is varied. A major feature of the climate is the long and often very severe winters usually with more than four months of snow. Rain is plentiful and evenly distributed. The proportion of species varies from site to site; in general, that of beech is greater on sunny or south-facing slopes than on the shaded, north-facing slopes. The storied structure usually has the conifers projecting above the broadleaved trees of the lower storey. Gaps in the stands are filled with young mixed regeneration.

On a favourable site the mean annual increment of a selection forest composed mainly of Norway spruce and European silver fir with some beech is 10-11 m^3 ha^{-1} $year^{-1}$, and the proportion of trees exceeding 50 cm in diameter at breast height can be very high. Thus, the diverse structure forest is productive, stable, and continuous and yet is capable of meeting markets where large size and high quality are greatly valued (Matthews, 1989).

Use in Britain

Britain has no examples of the 'true' selection stands found in central Europe, because it has no comparable mixed natural indigenous forests. This has not prevented a few British foresters from attempting to create single tree selection forest with the species and sites available to them (see Table 4.1). They have used light-demanding species like Scots pine or ash, moderate shade-bearers like sycamore or Douglas fir, and shade-bearers like grand fir, western hemlock or beech to provide components of the different canopy levels described earlier.

Another difficulty in Britain is that although foresters are familiar with the silvicultural characters of many species when grown pure, they are less informed about their behaviour in mixtures or in two-storied or multi-storied forest. So, attempts to use the selection systems have gone in two main directions: either to create mosaics of small groups or to proceed by underplanting to achieve several storeys. The four examples which follow suggest that both these routes are viable.

Table 4.1 The location of stands treated by the single tree and/or group selection systems.

	Wind zone [a]	Main soil type	Species	Age and conversion
Weasenham New Wood, Swaffham	3	Podzol	Mixed conifers	Various
Kyloe Wood, Berwick-on-Tweed	6	Brown earths and surface-water gleys	Mixed conifers	Various
Ipsden Estate, Oxfordshire	1	Clay-with-flint	Mixed conifers and broadleaves	40 years
Rossie Priory, Dundee	3-4	Brown earths	Mixed broadleaves	Various

[a] Wind zone describes the regional windiness for the site; values obtained from Quine and White (1993) and Quine (personal communications for areas in SE England). See Glossary 1 for further definition.

Weasenham New Wood, Norfolk

Weasenham New Wood is situated near Swaffham in west Norfolk. A stand of 20 ha is a well-established example of selection forest composed of mixed conifers (Douglas fir, Scots pine, larches, western red cedar, western hemlock and species of Silver fir) together with a few broadleaved trees. It is part group selection and part single tree selection. Access to the stand is well served by an intensive system of tracks.

This stand and the woods around it are the result of original thinking and skilled management by three generations of the Coke family. In the 1880s the second Earl of Leicester (grandfather of the present owner, Major R. L. Coke) planted west North American conifers on heathland with ironpan podzol in gaps among Scots pine self-seeded from old clumps. Many of the new plants were killed by frost, but after a gale in 1885 had removed most of the old trees, Scots pine and birch invaded the site. The New Wood was fenced against rabbits and in 1905 varied species of conifers were planted. In 1907 many more trees were planted, and all grew well to provide shelter and the backbone of today's New Wood. After 1920 more trees were added and natural regeneration was encouraged by making thinnings in the developing stand.

Weasenham New Wood was first substantially recorded by Paterson (1958) by which time it had evolved from a two-storied stand into an irregular stand with many species and several canopy levels. There was also a notable increase in the proportion of shade-bearing and moderate shade-bearing species. Establishment, initially by underplanting, was increasingly by natural regeneration, with some large gaps being provided to encourage regeneration of larches, which locally were the most valuable species. Selective fellings were made on a 3 to 5-year cycle.

The result of almost a century of management is a single tree-cum-group selection stand capable of sustained production of high-quality timber, with high amenity value, and encouragement of wildlife (front cover plate). Some of the best trees have been high-pruned, but the growth of the lower canopy and shading of stems has made this unnecessary for many other species. The intention is to continue to grow mainly conifers with a small number of broadleaves such as oak, sweet chestnut and birch in a diverse structure with no clear cutting. The New Wood is 'self-perpetuating' provided that the skilled management continues. It has great beauty, augmented by azaleas and hybrid rhododendrons at ride intersections. Major Coke affirms that 'the timber in the uneven-aged woods is far superior to that in his even-aged woods, and the former has suffered less from windthrow. The uneven-aged woods have also been considerably more profitable'. Major Coke's experience at Weasenham New Wood enabled him in 1980 to urge 'more irregular forestry in Britain' to a Government Select Committee on 'Scientific Aspects of Forestry'.

Kyloe Wood, Northumberland

Nine miles south of Berwick-on-Tweed, Kyloe Wood (391 ha) is owned by the Fleming family. It includes many fine conifer stands of diverse structure, consisting largely of maturing and mature overwood with an understorey of natural regeneration. The top canopy of conifers (chiefly Douglas fir, grand fir, Scots pine, western red cedar and western hemlock) were mainly planted in 1915 but some trees are older. Prolific western hemlock natural regeneration appeared following thinnings during the early 1970s and even more abundantly later in that decade (Plate 18). These thinnings and others made during the 1980s did some damage to the understorey but it was quickly made good by new regeneration.

There is a lack of 20 to 40-year-old trees. Some of the stands are now two-storied and irregular in appearance. Earlier attempts at group selection and the single tree selection systems were not successful. Almost all the mixed, two-storied or multi-canopied stands are dominated by western hemlock which is sometimes so aggressive as to prevent the survival of other species. For the past 20 years it has covered much of the forest floor in a dense mat often of about 2000 seedlings per square metre. Kyloe Wood could consist of western hemlock and Noble fir since the other species regenerating—notably Douglas fir, Scots pine, larch and western red cedar — provide only sporadic cover. The regeneration overall has been successful on the soils derived from sandstone and less frequent on the heavier clay soils.

The objectives of management are to maintain uneven-aged stands of mixed conifer species as well as notable specimen trees and to achieve sustained yield. The dominance of western hemlock poses problems in species diversity which will require intervention. The diverse, mixed, uneven-aged stands supplement a wide range of fine large conifers, many high-pruned and up to 90 years old. The whole forms a woodland of beauty and interest. Much credit is due to past foresters, notably Wilfred Fox.

Ipsden Estate, Oxfordshire

Ipsden Estate is part of the Chiltern beechwoods. The owner, M. G. Reade DSC (see Appendix 5), has consistently established what he describes as 'irregular selection forest intermediate between single tree selection and group selection' (Reade, 1957, 1960, 1965, 1990). The emphasis varies between one site and the next. At present, some areas (e.g. compartments 5 and 7) are conventional stands of mixed broadleaved species, although an attempt is made to diversify the age distribution by retaining some overwood. There are also areas (compartments 2 and 3)

predominantly of beech or oak which are developing the multi-storied condition of a selection forest, largely as a result of thinning, underplanting and natural regeneration. Continental recommendations are being followed in keeping natural regeneration in a suppressed state for periods of 20 years or more. The trees then tend to develop a characteristic flat-topped form, but are expected to respond to light when the overstorey is thinned. The treatment cycle is variable, usually between 6 and 12 years. In other areas a group selection structure is more apparent (as in compartment 10). The old trees in groups of 0.2 to 0.6 ha are heavily thinned and underplanted, usually with beech, oak, pine and grand fir. Oak grows strongly on the deeper clay-with-flint soils and outperforms beech.

Since 1953 Reade has monitored his woods by the 'Check' Method or *Méthode du Contrôle*, in this instance recording the number, species and stem diameter of all trees larger than 16 cm dbh at intervals of 6 to 10 years. About one-tenth of the 142 ha is enumerated, requiring about 3 man-hours per hectare. Local tariff tables are used to convert diameters to estimated volumes. The growing stock has been rising steadily in volume, and is expected to increase further for the next 30 to 40 years. Stabilising the growing-stock at a level compatible with the planned distribution of size-classes is the prime aim of management; but the interests of all other aspects and attributes of the forest are also considered.

Rossie Priory Estate, Angus

The Rossie Priory Estate, owned by the Honourable Mrs C. Best, daughter of Lord Kinnaird, lies about 9 miles west of Dundee. An uneven-aged and irregular stand in compartment 39 extends to 6 ha of mixed broadleaves growing on a deep moist brown earth. The main species was sycamore, and the older trees included beech, oak, ash and wych elm, about 170 years old, the remains of a former plantation. The stand was first substantially recorded by Paterson (1958) when ash and sycamore regeneration had occurred throughout, being abundant in clearings created by removal of old, unhealthy or defective trees. Group size was 0.1 to 0.2 ha and the edges were rapidly extended after successful regeneration. Temporary fencing against roe deer and rabbits was used frequently to protect the regeneration. The system which appeared to be best suited to the light-demanding behaviour of ash and sycamore created a mosaic of single-storied groups.

Although in 1958 the growing stock was well distributed over the size classes, there was a lack of information which would provide a reliable guide to treatments and fellings: periodic inventories and increment calculations would have been of value. Sadly, the stand was heavily damaged by a storm in 1968 but proved resilient. The storm created new clearings which were filled by dense regeneration of ash and sycamore. Attention to cleaning and thinning ensured that high quality poles of both species were recruited into the middle and upper canopy. The system can thus be applied to vigorous, light-demanding broadleaves provided that consistent, regular and positive silvicultural treatment is done. This example shows the value of retaining in mixed broadleaved stands some of the older trees to form a shelterwood for group regeneration, in this case of ash and sycamore and replanting of oak in patches.

Conclusions on the single tree selection system

1. *Light-demanders and shade-bearers.* The examples of Weasenham New Wood and Rossie Priory Estate have been managed for many years to encourage diversity through use of selection forest principles. Although the Weasenham New Wood is largely coniferous and Rossie Priory was composed of broadleaves, the former still contains, and the latter did contain, an important element of light-demanding species providing good timber readily marketed. Thus, they com-bined features of group selection and single tree selection; and Weasenham New Wood, given continued care, will remain as multi-storied mixtures of light-demanders, moderate shade-bearers and shade-bearers. It is significant that both stands traversed a period when they were two-storied, and it may be that creating two-storied high forest is a possible or even a desirable route to single tree selection forest.

2. *Creating mosaics.* Ipsden Estate and Kyloe Wood provide two contrasting examples. In the former, the owner has a wide variety of soils to contend with and conversion may have been from scrub and poor quality woodlands to something better. Parts of Kyloe Wood have to contend with an aggressive shade-enduring climax species, western hemlock, and the few examples of attempted selection forest are reverting to even-aged stands chiefly of that species and some of grand fir.

3. *Soil preferences.* Selection forest can be created on soils ranging from podzols with iron-pan to deep moist brown earths. So far, it has been thought that selection forest should be attempted only on fertile sheltered sites but this may not always be so. However, sites with high windthrow possibilities, and wet soils, should be avoided.

4. *Influence of soil texture on natural regeneration.* Natural regeneration is more plentiful on soils of light texture than on heavier soils, perhaps due to lesser weed growth, and often appears after disturbance of the canopy by thinnings and skidder extraction.

5. *Achieving the balance in broadleaved selection forest.* For broadleaved selection forest there must be at least one, and preferably two, light-demanding species that produce valuable timber. If there are two shade-enduring species in the mixture, they must be controlled. This is done by denying light until the one that needs more light is well established, or by removing some of them before they get too numerous.

6. *Trial and error period*. There has to be a period of trial and error before a suitable form of selection forest is found for each set of site conditions. However, it seems that multi-storied structure, suitably stocked with compatible species, will be useful although likely to fall half-way between single tree selection and group selection.

7. *Importance of inventory*. It is important to have initial and subsequent inventory to measure the development of the stands and to guide the application of thin/fell to lead towards the ideal stem-number curve (see Appendix 3). British examples have been conducted without this; an important exception is at Ipsden, by Reade.

8. *Continuity of management*. The benefit of continuity of management is patently demonstrated at Weasenham.

Chapter 5
Other silvicultural systems

The four silvicultural systems considered in this chapter are: two-storied high forest, high forest with reserves, coppice and coppice with standards; also included is restructuring extensive conifer forest by patch clear cutting. Particular reference is given to the Chilterns as being an important beechwood region requiring special treatment for structure, access, recreation, wildlife conservation and landscape. Table 5.1 gives examples of stands treated by these systems.

Two-storied high forest

This system is composed of an upper and lower storey of trees growing on the same site. Generally, two species are involved, the upper storey usually comprising a light-demander under which a shade-tolerant species can grow without being suppressed when introduced at a later date. Trees of the upper storey are treated as an even-aged stand in terms of stocking and thinning until they approach

Table 5.1 The location of stands treated by other silvicultural systems.

	Wind zone[a]	Main species
Two-storied high forest		
Dartington, Devon	2	Japanese larch over western hemlock, western red cedar and Douglas fir
High forest with reserves		
Longleat, Wiltshire	2	Douglas fir and larch
Bolderwood, New Forest, Hampshire	2-3	Douglas fir
Reelig Glen, near Inverness, Inverness-shire	4	Douglas fir and mixed conifers
Plodda Falls, Guinsachan, Inverness-shire	4	Douglas fir
Coppice and coppice with standards		
Numerous examples available in south-east and south-west England		Broadleaves
Restructuring by patch clear cutting		
Kielder, Northumberland	5-6	Sitka spruce
North York Moors District	3-4	Sitka spruce
Restructuring by (mainly) group regeneration		
The Chilterns, Buckinghamshire, Hertfordshire, Oxfordshire, Bedfordshire	1	Beech

[a] Wind zone describes the regional windiness for the site; values obtained from Quine and White (1993) and Quine (personal communications for areas in SE England). See Glossary 1 for further definition.

mid-rotation, when a final heavy thinning and possibly some high pruning takes place. At this stage, the stand is underplanted with a shade-tolerant species; occasionally the lower storey is established through natural regeneration before or soon after the heavy thinning. Both storeys are allowed to grow up and subsequent thinnings are undertaken in the lower storey. They may be felled together, or the upper storey may be removed to leave the lower as an even-aged maturing stand. Two-storied high forest is frequently limited to only one rotation because of the difficulty of forming a second understorey under the previous shade-tolerant one. The trees to be retained must be prepared for this several years in advance so that they develop strongly tapered stems and good root systems, and this implies early commitment to the establishment of a lower storey rather than reliance on the system to resolve a silvicultural or management difficulty at some later stage.

The advantages of two-storied high forest according to Matthews (1989) are:

- The lower storey protects the soil, controls weeds and gives freedom to thin the upper storey heavily to encourage the best stems to add increment.

- The upper storey provides protective cover for establishing those shade-tolerant species which are subject to frost damage.

- Where a mixed stand is required but the growth rates of the species differ, the system can be used to give the slower growing species an early start.

- There may be early income from the final heavy thinning at a time when the trees are still of moderate size.

- The system can be used to effect a gradual change of species and products through the lower storey.

- At least in its early stages the visual appearance can be pleasing.

The disadvantages of the system include: in windy climates the sudden exposure of the upper storey by the heavy thinning can result in windthrow even on brown earths; when the upper storey trees reach the age of final felling,

damage can occur to the lower storey unless care is taken (appropriate thinning of the lower storey will allow felling into prepared gaps); and the system is more difficult to manage than a uniform even-aged one, both in terms of balancing the growth of each storey and in carrying out regeneration and tending operations.

On the Continent, the most common reason for using the system is to encourage diameter increment in selected upper storey trees while protecting the soil with the lower storey. The objective is most frequently met where Scots pine is underplanted with European silver fir, Douglas fir or Norway spruce; or where Scots pine or oak is underplanted with beech. Miegroet (1962), after studying two-storied high forest stands for small estates in Belgium, calculated minimum areas for regeneration, tending and economic management. For areas of 5 ha or less, he considered the system was promising, using as the upper storey light-demanding species with rapid growth and short rotations, such as ash, sycamore and wild cherry, and as the lower storey Douglas fir, western hemlock and grand fir.

Dartington, Devon

In the 1950s W. E. Hiley (1956, 1959, 1964, 1967) experimented with two-storied high forest. He wished to grow Japanese larch to large diameters but noted that in well-stocked stands current annual diameter increment culminated quite soon; and in order to maintain rapid growth in diameter the trees needed large crowns, requiring virtual isolation at an early age. Hiley decided that underplanting with a shade-tolerant species would make fuller use of the site while allowing rapid growth of the Japanese larch. He had hoped to exploit a strong local market for mining timber with the produce from the heavy thinning of the upper storey, avoid less profitable later thinnings and combine the advantages of two-storey forest with the economies of the clear cutting system.

Site protection and weed suppression were to be achieved by means of the lower storey of shade-tolerant species which would be tended as an even-aged stand.

In pursuance of those objectives, in 1955 Hiley heavily thinned a compartment of 25-year-old Japanese larch to 120 stems ha^{-1} and underplanted with western hemlock, western red cedar and Douglas fir (Howell *et al.*, 1983). The first two species succeeded in the under-storey but the Douglas fir did not. Although Hiley achieved his silvicultural and marketing objectives in the two-storied stand, his financial predictions proved optimistic. The system was discontinued after 1965, partly due to changes in the dimensions of timber required by the local mining market. Hiley, besides proving that the overstorey must be further reduced if Douglas fir is to grow healthily as an under-storey, saw several benefits in the two-storied system. The ground is never completely uncovered and a small selection of the best trees is given the necessary room for rapid growth in the overstorey. The system enables adjustment of the distribution of age classes within a stand. Where there is an excess of young age classes, early maturation of the open upper storey provides a final crop sooner than is possible in a dense uniform stand. Moreover, the lower storey helps to fill the gap in the distribution of size classes which may otherwise be caused by not having any land to plant. Historically, it was thought that some species were 'incapable of maintaining soil fertility' and that growing a lower storey of a different, usually broadleaved, species would help to protect the soil from degrade. However, at Dartington, the poorer sites gave little gain and did not justify establishing a lower storey (Howell *et al.*, 1983; Matthews, 1989).

Two-storied high forest can provide a quick route to selection forest. As an example, take a 30 to 40-year-old stand of larch. Thin to variable intensities to suit the species to be under-planted in groups, i.e. to 300 stems ha^{-1} for beech and grand fir; and 100 stems ha^{-1} for Scots pine, ash and sycamore. Allow the underplant groups to grow on for 15 to 20 years, progressively felling more of the overstorey, and cleaning and thinning the groups as required. Then, make space for further group planting by felling more upper storey larch, encouraging natural regeneration of larch and introducing more species such as Douglas fir and Norway spruce. The size of the groups should not be less than 0.5 ha and preferably larger for the light-demanders. The total time for conversion would be approximately 30 years, at which time the forester will have to decide on the principal species.

High forest with reserves

This is produced by retaining selected trees of a parent stand over a young crop established below it through natural regeneration. These large trees, known as 'reserves', may be retained, scattered or in small groups, for the whole or part of a second rotation. The objective is for them to add increment and produce large-sized timber for use in boat-building and construction and some to produce veneer quality. Thus, reserves are normally of species in demand for those purposes, such as Scots pine, European larch, Douglas fir and oak. Reserves may also act as seedbearers to fill blanks in young crops. Other important benefits are amenity by producing stands with a degree of natural appearance and increasing diversity.

The selection of reserves requires care. Large trees suddenly isolated are liable to be thrown by wind or in certain cases become unhealthy; and hence reserves should be of windfirm species and have well-tapered stems, in addition to strong crowns and firm root systems. Trees in some instances are prepared for isolation by selecting prospective reserves many years ahead so that they may receive special attention during thinnings. Oak is often retained as a reserve, but is liable to become stag-headed and produce epicormic branches when isolated. Beech is generally unsuitable, as it has a heavy crown and is liable to sun-scorch when suddenly isolated. Spruces are generally unsuitable. Douglas fir can be accepted in reasonably sheltered areas.

Advantages and disadvantages of high forest with reserves are somewhat similar to those of two-storied high forest although harvesting damage to natural regeneration and underplanting is less. The greatest danger being the possibility of windthrow has resulted in a decline in the use of the system following some major storms on the Continent during the past 20 years. In France, this system is infrequently used, whereas in Germany it is more common. Four notable examples in Britain are outlined below.

Longleat, Wiltshire

In this adaption of the system small areas of large Douglas firs and larches are retained as reserves, for amenity and landscape purposes, to serve as seedbearers, and to add value increment; some trees are intended to become 'monarchs of the forest'. Windthrow is usually a risk.

Reelig Glen, Inverness-shire

At Reelig Glen near Inverness, Douglas fir is a major constituent of a mixed and somewhat diverse structure stand growing on a fertile, moist and sheltered site. It is also popular with the public because of the varied habitat and range of bird life (M. Rodgers, personal communication).

Plodda Falls, Inverness-shire

The third example with Douglas fir is at Plodda Falls near Guisachan.

Bolderwood, New Forest, Hampshire

At Bolderwood the reserved Douglas fir have commanded very high prices as ships' masts and for large flag poles.

Coppice and coppice with standards

The systems of broadleaved coppice and coppice with standards (nowadays used mainly in England, but previously also in Wales and Scotland) are well known. For general accounts of them and associated techniques of silviculture, the reader is referred to Rackham (1980), Peterken (1981), Evans (1984), Pryor and Savill (1986), Crowther and Evans (1986), Matthews (1989), Hart (1991) and Buckley (1992). Both systems are always the result of human management and are applicable mainly to sweet chestnut, oak, ash, lime and hazel. That of pure coppice, when used for sustained yield, led to the idea of rotations to suit different species and local markets, and to the practice of felling in roughly equal and contiguous annual 'cants' which together made up a felling series.

Coppice with standards met so many needs of the medieval rural economy that it was soon systematised into a carefully managed underwood of selected species such as hazel and lime (later expanded to sweet chestnut coppice by planting that species), and of an overwood with a balanced growing stock of standards comprising chiefly oak, sweet chestnut and ash. The conversion of coppice to high forest, by 'storing', is an alternative management system for most species of coppice, but in Britain such conversion has been effected predominantly through neglect or from decline in markets for the coppice products.

The two coppice systems are now regarded as being among the most desirable silvicultural treatments of broadleaves from the viewpoint of nature conservation on lowland sites. When standards are present, particularly if they are diverse in age, they not only provide a deep canopy but also continuity of woodland conditions. In addition they have attributes for landscape, whereas pure coppice — although it supplies benefits of plantlife conservation — can over time be temporarily undesirable scenically, if too dominant in the local landscape; the bare ground condition is repeated much more frequently than with high forest. Coppice occasionally can be thinned, especially if the introduction of light would have beneficial effects on yield/size of produce or nature conservation. Coppice woods can thus be managed on a kind of selection basis (the coppice selection system: Matthews, 1989), with a range of ages of regrowth on the same area, giving greater continuity of woodland cover and more internal structural diversity than conventional coppice. This procedure, though requiring extra management, may have advantages for landscape and wildlife. Conservationists present a strong case for the retention of the coppice systems as they are the traditional management for many of Britain's broadleaved woodlands and that which gives high biological diversity.

Many older broadleaved stands have the appearance of high forest but actually are of coppice or pollard origin. When the main demand for coppice products almost ceased around the 1920s, the stems/poles were left to grow on to full size trees that had some sale value. The timber yield from these 'stored coppice' stands is similar to comparable high forest stands, though quality, particularly in the base of the tree, may be inferior. Coppicing may be possible in these stands, even after 100 years.

Restructuring extensive conifer forest by patch clear cutting

The concept of introducing diversity into extensive uniform even-aged State conifer forest by restructuring using medium-sized patch clear cut coupes was initiated by a Forestry Commission Conservator, J. A. Spencer, in north-east England in the early 1980s. The stimulus to restructuring can be associated with the realisation that additional land will not be released to forest use around a given holding/district, and plans must be laid to obtain a sustained yield and forecasted supplies of small diameter roundwood and sawlogs. Concentrating the felling into 10-15 years would not serve these objectives. Elsewhere in State forests, restructuring giving rise to diverse structure tended to be initiated either by landscape plans whereby stands were reserved to improve the design (e.g.

Thetford Chase, Norfolk), or by major recreational pressure (e.g. Grizedale, Cumbria).

Restructuring uniform even-aged conifer forest in the uplands using patch clear cutting (as well as some other methods of regeneration), patch size being varied according to altitude and aspect, is now progressing, adhering to felling and landscape design plans. These are relatively recent attempts, and it is uncertain that the planned structure will be fully achieved owing to the unpredictable effects of windthrow and lack of preparation of coupe edge. In north-east England, two good examples of such restructuring by Forest Enterprise are Kielder Forest and North York Moors District.

Kielder, Northumberland

This extensive State forest, managed by Forest Enterprise, consists mainly of 40 to 50-year-old Sitka and Norway spruce (Plate 19). It is managed under a design plan to restructure uniform even-aged plantations of the first rotation into diverse structure to serve increasingly multiple purpose objectives. The design concepts are a reflection both of the physical limitations imposed by windthrow and the site (gley soils) and the aim to achieve a reasonable balance between timber production and environmental enhancement (McIntosh, 1991). The design plan seeks to integrate the requirements of efficient operational activities with a planned increase in wildlife and landscape diversity. The current extents of felling coupes by altitudinal zone are generally 5-10 ha in the valley bottom, 15-45 ha on the mid slopes and 50-100 ha on the upper slopes.

The main elements in the process of restructuring are the identification and design of future felling coupes, manipulation of the felling dates to achieve a 'patchwork quilt' pattern of stands of different ages, indefinite retention of a small proportion of stands, subject to possible windthrow, and the introduction of both broadleaved trees and open space. Considerable commitment and planning are required to achieve the objectives set, and costs are incurred (mainly loss of some revenue from timber production), but these relate largely to the first rotation. If some of the age-class manipulation can be achieved in this period, then subsequent felling can take place at nearer the optimum economic time without adversely affecting the desired pattern. It is not known what the effect of this design will be on windflow patterns over the Forest, but the increased roughness may cause more turbulence and the risk of windthrow may be increased.

The whole is a conventional clear cutting system but with constraints on the size of the coupe and the timing of its felling in relation to surrounding coupes. It will be interesting to see whether the pressure over time is to simply reduce the size of the coupes without changing the basic silvicultural system of clear cutting; already there are areas where the system is not sensitive enough and where more traditional continuous forest cover systems are planned. There appears to be scope for more use of natural regeneration in smaller groups on sites where weed re-colonisation is slow.

North York Moors District

This eastern heathland area of some 19 000 ha, under Forest Enterprise management, presents examples of two forms of uneven-aged forest structure (J. MacKenzie, personal communication). The site conditions contribute to relatively good stability; there are brown earths and podzols on the scarp slopes and extensive ironpan soils over the plateaux, with pine and larch stands dominant at middle to late pole stages. This gives the opportunity for implementing systems alternative to large scale clear cutting through the use of natural regeneration or by underplanting following preparatory heavy late pole-stage thinning. More gradual replacement also favours long-term log supply to sawmills as the total forest area in the District is not expanding significantly owing to the constraints on land use in the National Park.

Firstly, the more long standing practice of restructuring is used, similar to the system recently being undertaken at Kielder Forest, but in the North York Moors and Hamsterley Forest in south Durham (Plate 20) the scale is smaller, resulting in the development of a more intricate mosaic forest structure. Clear fell coupes vary from 3 ha to, occasionally, as much as 25 ha, and have been replanted. Natural regeneration has appeared on many occasions and supplemented planting. Where practicable, the size and shape take into account the principles of forest design pertaining to land form, scale and prominence in the local landscape. This system suits the management of the light-demanding species growing in these forest areas, namely larches, pines and Sitka spruce.

Secondly, consideration is being given to the introduction of more intensive selection silvicultural systems to provide a degree of naturalness in a few areas, particularly where adjacent to recreation facilities. This could not be introduced on a large scale because of the need for operating cost-effective management systems; but there is scope for small scale development of such stand structures along selected edge zones on forest walks or public rights of way, as well as applying it to larger areas of stands which have a high usage by the public.

In the North York Moors the problem lies in the effective application of these more visually attractive and more intensively managed systems within stands of light-demanding species, such as pines and larches. This would normally be done by uniform seeding felling or group shelterwood but there have been considerable windthrow losses on ploughed ironpan soils. A trial has been established to introduce a group selection system into a heavily thinned Scots pine stand at Dalby Forest. Also at Dalby and in Cropton Forest, two-tiered larch stands are to be managed to develop further diverse structure on a group basis.

Where Douglas fir already occurs in appropriate areas there is more scope for the development of selection systems as initially

Douglas fir is more tolerant of some shade when young than pine or larch. At Hamsterley and Dalby Forests, management for diversity of structure on a small scale has been introduced into selected stands where natural regeneration has occurred. The same principle is being considered for suitable stands of grand fir and western hemlock at Hamsterley and Wykeham Forests.

Another possible variant is to achieve a diverse structure in pine stands within a heathland ecosystem, the aim being to allow a more open stand to develop to encourage *Calluna* and *Vaccinium* to be sustained by manipulating natural regeneration of pine. This could suit the North York Moors National Park's policies for woodland by developing a more natural transition zone between forest and moorland, as well as within appropriate open 'space zones' in the forest. Other examples of restructuring by patch clear cutting are with Corsican pine at Thetford Chase (Norfolk) and with larch and mixed conifers at Grizedale (Cumbria).

Restructuring beechwoods by (mainly) group regeneration

The example chosen to illustrate this form of restructuring is the Chilterns. This is an important woodland region requiring special silvicultural treatment for timber production, structure, access, recreation, wildlife conservation and landscape. It can be regarded as attempting group shelterwood restocking on an extensive scale in multiple ownerships.

The Chilterns, Hertfordshire/Buckinghamshire/ Bedfordshire/Oxfordshire

The largest area of beechwoods in Britain, the Chilterns, provides examples of the need for and use of regeneration. Its woodlands are often wrongly cited as an example of 'selection forest'. Several centuries ago, the French practice of *furetage* was followed. This is really an 'exploitation felling', single good quality trees being removed here and there in an unregulated way, resulting in impoverishment of the stand. Jones (1952) gives historical and silvicultural evidence which shows that 'exploitation felling', rather than true selection management, has dominated these woods for the last few centuries. The woodlands were steadily creamed of the best timber-sized beech (along with smaller poles for wood turners or 'bodgers') as well as almost all the oak. Some of the stands are of coppice origin.

The Chilterns include numerous stands of beechwoods (Plates 21, 22 and 23), some State and many others in private hands. Predominantly of beech, there are also good oak, ash and wild cherry. Sycamore, birch and hornbeam are present in some areas. Less frequently, introduced conifers are found — European larch, western hemlock and western red cedar, and occasionally Norway spruce, grand fir, Douglas fir and coast redwood — all helpful for diversification, amenity and conservation reasons (K. Wallis, personal communication). Beech regenerates naturally, but rarely predictably, and has to compete with several damaging agents including frost, deer, rabbits, grey squirrel, voles, wood-pigeons and insects. The provenance of the beech is not good, probably due either to poor genotype from selective exploitation or to unsuitable past management, so phenotypes are poor. However, some users of the timber assert that it is whiter and more flexible than that grown elsewhere.

Many of the beechwoods have been allowed to grow to financial maturity and beyond without any form of controlled replacement or conversion. From the age of about 130 years, depending on site conditions, beech on the heavier plateau soils start to deteriorate; this process begins earlier and, especially following droughts, can be more rapid on the poorer soils of the scarp and combe sides. The result can be serious deterioration of the amenity, conservation, landscape and recreational values of the woods, as well as of timber production.

Almost half of the Chiltern woodlands are mature or over-mature. They are remarkably even-aged with very few stands in the age range 30-80 years, being more in the range of 80-150 years, with a few trees reaching 180 years. Some good quality stands exist, but the general impression is one of even-aged stands of low quality and poor stocking, lacking diverse age and size structure, and now in deteriorating health in parts.

The increasingly strong public pressure on the Chilterns for access, recreation and landscape retention has raised concern about how best to perpetuate this important woodland region (Penistan, 1974; Evans, 1984; Tilney-Bassett, 1988). The Chiltern Plan (Chilterns Standing Conference, 1971, 1988, 1993) advocated that the beechwoods should be managed with the objective of perpetuating a broadleaved forest. The emphasis would be on beech where appropriate, and on limiting the area of each coupe to about 1 ha and to spread the regeneration of individual larger woods (8 ha or more) over a period of 30-40 years. Conifers would be allowed as nurses provided they did not prejudice the main principle. In some areas of high conservation value, the coupe size would be limited to 0.5 ha.

Throughout this century, continual attempts to manage the numerous component stands of the Chiltern woodlands on a so-called 'selection system' mostly failed, resulting in the urgency during recent decades to regenerate effectively large areas of such stands. For the bulk of the over-mature stands the only management option is to fell and restock them, either by planting or natural seeding (despite its problems) or a mixture of the two. In stands where only some trees appear unhealthy and lacking in vigour, group shelterwood fellings of the poorest parts can be carried out to diversify structure, the size of opening generally being 0.2-0.4 ha, though it may extend to over 1 ha. In stands which appear completely healthy and still growing vigorously, very careful thinning may be carried out with a view to preparing for their regeneration in 20 to 30 years' time. The use of natural regeneration has been successful on several sites but it is not generally followed owing to

its uncertainty (beech mast frequency being some 5 to 7 years). Where natural regeneration arises at the time of felling, it can be used to advantage but, in general, planting — typically with mixtures of beech, oak, ash, wild cherry and European larch — is the main means of re-establishment. Other relevant Forest Enterprise diverse structure stands on the Chilterns are at Queen Wood (see Chapter 2). (Private sector examples on the Chilterns by Bourne, Garfitt, and Reade have been noted earlier in Chapters 2 and 3.)

Conclusions on other silvicultural systems

1. *Two-storied high forest* can provide a relatively quick route to selection forest on suitable sites.

2. *High forest with reserves* can provide stands with a degree of natural appearance and interesting diversity, the greatest danger being the possibility of windthrow.

3. *Coppice and coppice with standards* are considered to be among the most desirable silvicultural systems from the point of view of nature conservation on lowland sites, and continuity of woodland conditions. Good spatial planning of the coupes can improve structural diversity.

4. *Restructuring extensive conifer forest by patch clear cutting* gives rise to diverse structure; it should adhere to felling and landscape designs. The effects of windthrow and coupe edge preparation are pertinent. Mosaics of small patch clear cutting which are naturally regenerated would greatly soften the impact of the restocking stage on conservation and landscape. Such restructuring is now very widely applied, and is certain to increase.

5. *The Chiltern beechwoods* contain examples of the treatments necessary for regenerating large areas of environmentally sensitive, aged, low quality broadleaved woodlands in the south of England. Forms of group shelterwood and group selection seem most appropriate, given adequate protection.

Chapter 6
The economics of irregular forestry

Introduction

Economic analyses of forestry until recent years have been chiefly an assessment of *financial yield,* reflecting that forestry has, in the past, predominantly been directed at profitable timber production. With an environmentally aware society there is increasing interest in non-wood benefits, which often complement timber production. There is increasing need for these benefits to be taken into account by economic analysis which could lead to changes in methods of silviculture, stand structure, species choice and rotation.

A wide range of silvicultural options should be tested; and analyses are required to determine optimal, desirable, or at least acceptable silvicultural systems on specific sites, and for desired objectives. The implicit objective, at least of State forestry, is to make forests useful to society. Social returns are affected by a complex range of factors including: land capability, nature conservation attributes, recreation potential, landscape, and watershed characteristics. The overall social objective is still to operate so that the value of benefits derived from a forest exceeds the costs expended, but now social and environmental factors should be brought within the decision-making process.

One of the contenders for fresh appraisal is uneven-aged diverse structure forest. In its widest sense this comprises a group of silvicultural systems that have not been practised to any significant extent in Britain, although they have long been practised successfully in western and central Europe. In making these new, wider assessments, objectives of forestry must be clearly stated and the value of alternative silvicultural systems estimated against them (Whiteman, 1991).

Economic analysis, and discounting in particular, has never featured as much in Continental forestry as it has in Britain, although it originated around 1849 in Germany. Continental foresters have not needed discounting to manage existing, often natural forests: the felling of mature stands provides profit and pays for restocking. In Britain, renewal of the forest resource has required the injection of capital and this has been charged by discounting. The economics of forestry are highly dependent on the discount rate employed, and the values which are accorded to non-wood benefits (Price, 1989; Worrell, 1991). These are not unique to uneven-aged forest, but are likely to be especially important due to:

1. the assumed higher value of non-wood benefits which frequently may be expected;

2. the financial loss which may be sustained during any conversion period.

The most commonly assumed objective of most State forestry until recent years was that of maximising net discounted revenue (NDR); and profitability remains of central importance, even when some of the benefits are non-financial. Therefore, careful economic comparison is needed of costs and revenues between uniform and uneven-aged systems (Lorrain-Smith, 1986). The following questions need to be addressed:

- In irregular forestry does management cost more per unit area, e.g. because of relatively small scale, complexity of working and other management decisions, and the need for additional operations or higher overheads (i.e. management time)?

- Are volume and value production and quality of timber higher or lower and is there a different assortment of sizes?
- Are timber prices affected (much will depend on the rotation), for example by small scale and mixed assortments?
- Are the timing of costs and receipts different between the two systems?
- Do better non-wood benefits accrue to the State and society or to the private owner?
- What is the influence on cash flow (stored capital)?

Answers to these questions will only be acceptable when they are based on adequate data. Evidence from Glentress Forest suggests that costs of establishment may be up to 50% higher when planting is the method of regeneration, and of harvesting 10-20% higher, than Forestry Commission standard rates (Shrimpton, 1986, 1988). Compensatory are the increased values of amenity, landscape, wildlife conservation and forest recreation.

The single tree selection system

Estimates of costs or revenues have rarely been published from uneven-aged stands in Britain, but net timber revenues per hectare are likely to be lower than in the clear cutting system due to the need for directional felling, the increased care needed in extraction, and the diversity of size assortment and species of marketable trees. Where a selection forest is already fully established, annual management and tending costs known, as well as the volume and value of the sustainable yield, it is possible to compare its financial yield with that of a forest under the clear cutting system. Experience is needed in order to be sure of these factors, but modelling could help this work in advance of empirical knowledge.

There has been debate as to the relative quality and value of timber produced under the selection system. The trees grow under relatively sheltered conditions, and receive a degree of shade in the early years, the effect being to reduce (a) early growth rates/ring width, and thereby the size of the juvenile core, and (b) the amount of reaction wood. The system is likely to increase the straightness of stems and reduce the number and size of lateral branches. However, in later years when a dominant tree becomes more exposed, there is likely to be an increase in the amount of taper, as well as ring width, and, depending on the species, stocking and any artificial pruning, there may be more live branches and hence larger knots in the crown wood and on trees on the edge of any groups (Helliwell, 1982); this would be apparent in the crown rather than in the more valuable butt lengths but these effects on wood quality may affect revenue.

Debate has also occurred about the total volume production of even-aged forest compared with uneven-aged forest (Savill and Evans, 1986). Productivity depends upon the species that are grown because there are differences in efficiency of assimilation between species and even between genotypes of the same species on the same site. In the selection system there may be greater productivity due to more efficient utilisation of incident light, and other resources, by the multi-storied canopy. The proportion of small-sized timber production is probably lower, and the maintenance of continuous forest cover means that the periods of low current annual increment at the beginning of the rotation of an even-aged stand are largely avoided.

The conflicting evidence was reviewed by Johnston *et al.* (1967), Johnston (1978) and Helliwell (1982) but no clear conclusions are evident. Differences in timber value are likely to be more important. There has also been considerable discussion on size assortments and it is usual that a much higher proportion of the total volume production of selection forest is in large sizes, and hence high value, compared with uniform stands. However, further research in this area is required (see Appendix 3).

Price (1989) lists claimed financial advantages of uneven-aged stands (significantly the selection system), relating particularly to assumed increased yield, better quality of timber, reduced susceptibility to storms and improvement of site by lesser soil insolation. He claims the system can save much cost of insecticide treatment, sometimes necessary in conifers when regenerating under the clear cutting system, there being a low density of felled tree stumps, and the population 'explosion' of pine weevil and black pine beetle does not occur. On the other hand, Price lists claimed financial disadvantages: the difficult, small-scale harvesting and more dispersed working; extending rotations; planting low-yielding species to promote environmental interest; or leaving areas unplanted for informal recreation. However, he notes that even-aged forest could suffer these penalties also in areas of high social pressure.

To create any form of uneven-aged structure takes significant time. Creation by afforestation could take several decades and entail major financial penalty by delayed planting, extended rotations or felling of immature stands. Conversion of a uniform even-aged pole-stage stand entails felling some trees before optimal rotation and prolonged retention of other trees that may become financially over-mature. The opportunity costs can be abated by spreading conversion over several rotations, so that no tree is ever felled significantly early or late, but the advantages of uneven-aged forestry are then very long delayed (Price, 1989).

The shelterwood uniform and group systems

These systems differ in several ways from the clear cutting and selection systems. The absence of uniformity will increase the management costs. However, the division of a forest management unit into a number of different age- or size-class stands should give a more uniform distribution of costs and revenues through time. The shelterwood group system would have a similar cash flow to that of a shelterwood uniform system, although the regeneration period would be longer and the management expenses during the period greater. A group system would probably be little different from a selection system in costs and revenues, provided the whole forest is divided up into several different age or size classes, so that their regeneration periods overlap. Over the forest as a whole this would result in similar annual costs and revenues.

The economic justification of uneven-aged and continuous forest cover

Texts touching on the economics of uneven-aged forest mostly agree that operations within it are more expensive than in even-aged forest, but there is disagreement about the degree of such differences.

Matthews (1986, 1989) found that the evidence gathered by several Continental foresters suggested that uneven-aged stands produced about the same or slightly less timber than even-aged stands on similar sites, and that foresters were consistent in their claims of higher monetary yields due to the superior qualities of the timber. Specific tentative claims about the costs of restructuring State forests in Britain include:

1. At Afon in Wales, where Forest Enterprise are restructuring upland conifer forest, Farmer (1991) expected the discounted revenue of timber foregone to be about 15% compared with clear cutting.

2. Greig (1990) suggests that Forest Enterprise conversion or restructuring of 15 separate lowland pine forests might be achieved for less than £5 ha^{-1} year^{-1} in profit foregone from timber production.

Whiteman (1991) sets out an economic framework for evaluating different silvicultural systems in State conifer forests including non-wood benefits. He suggests the likely levels of costs under each possible system, estimates the unpriced benefits to society, and concludes that diverse structure or continuous forest cover may in some cases be justified but that this is very sensitive to the method of assessing non-wood benefits; hence further research on methods to value these benefits is required. This deficiency is gradually being rectified by research, e.g. Shrimpton (1986, 1988), Pryor and Savill (1986), Benson and Willis (1992), Willis and Garrod (1992). A better economic case for alternative silvicultural systems is made when appropriate data and analyses have been developed and are accepted.

Conclusions on the economics of irregular forestry

1. *Overriding factors.* Initial conclusions would seem to suggest that silvicultural, aesthetic and environmental reasons rather than economic viability may be the overriding factors in determining the extent of continuous forest cover in Britain. Where an uneven-aged system will produce high-quality timber at a regular and sustained level without a large increase in costs, it may appeal to the State and other owners. This will also be the case where the benefits are high, if it is possible for the owner to capture some revenue from them as, for example, from commercial recreation. It should be easier to justify the cases where forest is owned and managed on behalf of the State, because its owners will be acting wholly in society's interests. Until conflicting objectives, and the ranking of them, are clarified, economics can only partially solve the problem of deciding which different uneven-aged systems could be used (Whiteman, 1991) and a fully convincing *economic* case can be made for them in Britain (see Appendix 3).

2. *Importance of the starting point.* The practice of conversion much depends on the starting point. Some foresters have started from (a) uniform even-aged woodland (likely to pay for itself); others from (b) unmanaged woodland or (c) scrub (both bound to be expensive).

Chapter 7

Influence of environmental factors on alternative silvicultural systems and conversion

The term 'conversion' is taken to mean a change from the even-aged clear cutting system to an alternative system more diverse in stand structure and species. In most conversions (and in restructuring) the main constraints are protecting the forest from the ravages of wind and damaging mammals. At the same time conversions have an impact on landscape, nature conservation and recreational potential. A desirable element, where possible, is natural regeneration.

Effect of wind

The severity of Britain's wind climate is important when discussing appropriate silvicultural systems, many of which originate from continental Europe. Britain's wind climate is dominated by the passage of Atlantic depressions, whose accumulated influence bring the strongest winds to the north and west of Britain; less common tracks bring strong winds to southern Britain. The general windiness is higher and the occurrence of damaging winds more common than on mainland Europe (see Figure 7.1).

Recent experience in Britain suggests that areas affected by gusts of 30–50 m s⁻¹ will experience sporadic damage to trees but that this will rarely total more than 1% of the forest area; areas affected by 35–40 m s⁻¹ knot gusts will experience significant damage with 1-10% of the forest over 12 m in height affected; areas affected by 40–45 m s⁻¹ gusts will experience catastrophic damage with 10-30% or more of the forest over 12 m in height affected (Quine, 1991). The return period for gusts of around 35 m s⁻¹ is 50 years on low lying sites in south-east England, approximately 5 years for mid slope sites in the Scottish Borders, and less than 5 years for similar sites in north Scotland.

The wind input into a silvicultural system is therefore dependent upon the region in which it is located i.e wind zone. Wind input also depends upon elevation, topographic position, and aspect relative to the prevailing winds (Quine and White, 1993). The character of the wind, e.g. gustiness, is conditioned by the local terrain upwind, e.g. open water, open country, forest.

The transition from one silvicultural system to another is likely to involve significant risk. Where the return periods or average interval between damaging storms are less than or of similar magnitude to the duration of the transition period then windthrow must be a serious consideration in decision-making. The answer is to begin early before the trees in the existing crops have reached a height that brings with it susceptibility to windthrow (see Chapter 3).

The windthrow hazard classification (Miller, 1985) was developed for even-aged stands subject to the clear cutting system. It gives a practical method of assessing windthrow vulnerability, and gives reasonable predictions of damage occurrence for use in management planning; refinements have been made (Quine and White, 1993; Quine and Wright, 1993). However, the application of the current classification to more sophisticated silvicultural systems is likely to be limited. While it will still provide valid comparisons of site vulnerability, the defined critical and terminal heights will not be appropriate.

Quine and Miller (1990) derived a set of recommendations for silvicultural systems and site type with reference to windthrow vulnerability (Table 7.1). Only the broad system

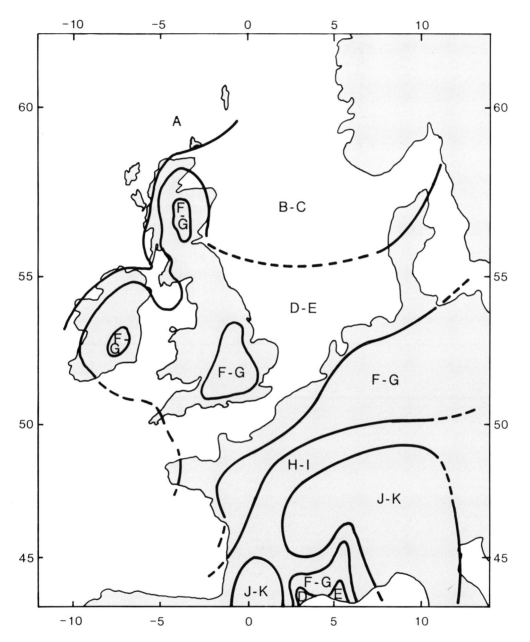

Figure 7.1 Wind zonation of Europe in the manner of the zonation of Britain included in the windthrow hazard classification. This is on scale of A (most windy) to K (least windy).

groups are covered, as it is impractical to allow for the many possible refinements to the systems. Windthrow hazard class (WHC) in this context is taken to reflect the frequency and strength of damaging winds, although in practice it also reflects soil-induced vulnerability.

The scope for choice of alternative systems on the high windthrow hazard classes 5-6 is limited, and is also constrained on the moderate windthrow hazard classes 3-4 because of the serious risk of windthrow. On the low windthrow hazard classes 1-2, choice of silvicultural systems will be largely determined by other factors, although perception of risk and recent experiences will undoubtedly influence decisions.

Effect of damaging mammals

Deer

Any silvicultural system dependent on regeneration either by planting or natural seeding must be free of excessive browsing and bark-stripping (Gill, 1992). Conversion of an even-aged stand to the establishment phase is the most difficult time when coping with deer, because of the sudden change in forest structure and consequent effects upon deer behaviour. Inadequate recognition of the latter and of the requirements of deer can pose severe problems for the forester. A relationship exists between forest structure and the population dynamics of all deer species. Sequential changes in forest structure are associated with stand succession from establishment to pre-thicket, thicket, and maturing and mature stages (Ratcliffe, 1988). On a local scale, pertinent issues are the relative palatability of species, stand vigour (and hence tolerance of browsing), site productivity, availability of alternative vegetation browse and the intimate distribution of shelter/cover and food supply.

Table 7.1 Appropriateness of silvicultural systems with reference to windthrow vulnerability of sites. (*Source*: Quine and Miller, 1990)

	Low hazard class sites e.g. WHC 1 and 2	Moderate hazard class sites e.g. WHC 3 and 4	High hazard class sites e.g. WHC 5 and 6
Clear fell without thinning	S[1]	S[1]	S[2&3]
Clear fell with thinning	S[2]	S[2]	U
Uniform shelterwood	S	U	U
Group shelterwood	S	U	U
Strip	S	S[3]	U
Wedge	S	S[3]	U
Selection	S	S	S[1]
Coppice	S	S	S[1]
Coppice with standards	S	U	U

S: Suitable. [1]Unlikely to be widely applicable; [2]consider diversification of age structure towards normality; [3]requires careful selection and alignment of edges and/or severance cuts.

U: Unsuitable.

Hill-Tout (1990) explains the factors relating to deer influencing the choice of silvicultural systems, especially concerning conifers in the uplands. Problems addressed and suggestions given for solving them include: fencing or individual protection is often inevitable for susceptible tree species in vulnerable situations; shooting is often effective in a comprehensive deer management strategy; and chemical repellents are generally ineffective. The whole of deer management should be seen as part of an integrated forest design strategy incorporating also timber production, nature conservation, landscape and recreational interests. Coupe size is pertinent; during their regeneration it is difficult and costly to reduce deer browse and bark-stripping in small coupes.

Grey squirrels

A deterrent to the successful economic growth of broadleaved stands of some species is the stripping of bark by grey squirrels. Control is necessary; this is not peculiar to uneven-aged systems though they prolong the period of risk. Methods of controlling populations are available and have been shown to be effective in preventing damage if properly applied and carried out at the right time although it has to be recognised that many woodland owners and farmers neglect to take the necessary action. High costs and many difficulties are experienced in growing some species of broadleaves in areas when populations of grey squirrel are high. Sycamore, beech, ash, birch and Norway maple are the most frequently and severely damaged. Oak and sweet chestnut are less frequently attacked and wild cherry is not often damaged. Of conifers, Scots, Corsican and lodgepole pine are the most frequently attacked. Thicket- and pole-stage trees aged 10 to 40 years are the most vulnerable. There is no evidence that damage is significantly greater or less between silvicultural systems.

Effects on landscape

Woods and forests are among the most attractive features of a landscape, their significance being related to location, topography, extent, outline, species, age, texture and colour.

Woods close to, or visible from, main roads or towns or scenic viewpoints have special importance as valued landscape features. One of the main reasons advanced for considering the use of diverse structure systems is the effect on the landscape. Sudden and drastic change is generally deplored by the public, whether it involves afforestation, line thinning, or extensive clear cutting. Gradual change is much more likely to be acceptable. Uniform even-aged high forest under the extensive *clear cutting system* is widely regarded as the least desirable for landscape value. The sudden lack of continuity of tree cover, and the change to bare ground with branchwood and stumps, are major disadvantages.

Shelterwood systems, and certain variants of *group systems*, achieve a degree of semi-permanency. They are most acceptable visually where trees have well-developed crowns and give a degree of coalescence. *Strip systems* can cause a significant adverse effect: coupes may appear 'moth-eaten' or fragmented and the geometric patterns are difficult to accommodate in the landscape, especially parallel linear openings perpendicular to the contours. In the *single tree selection system* full permanence of cover is achieved: the appearance as a whole remains unchanged; its visual advantages externally and internally are retained; and to the casual observer the woodland appearance remains constant. However, some people deplore the absence of a distant or even mid-length view. The *selection system* produces the greatest small scale diversity which itself may sometimes be monotonous if too extensive from the point of view of people walking in the forest, and the lack of views out; the views internally and to the outside can be inadequate. *Group systems* have a pleasing irregular appearance both during and after the regeneration period; the resulting young stands of trees often have an age range of 30 years or more.

Under the *clear cutting system*, in order to produce natural looking woodland landscapes, certain basic design criteria need to be satisfied even when using a *patch cutting system*. The key principles are shape, scale, and diversity, aiming to produce a pattern which reflects the characteristics of the landform (Crowe, 1978; McIntosh, E, 1990; Lucas, 1991; Forestry Commission, 1991, 1992; Bell, 1992). Time and space separation have to be used to create diversity by limiting the area to be clear cut in any one place and setting a period before an adjoining stand is felled and regenerated. The foregoing principles also apply to *shelterwood systems* based on group felling (in effect, felling of small coupes), because of the textural and tree height variations between management areas. Both the external and internal appearance of the forest should be considered in the design process. McIntosh (1991), the Forestry Commission (1991, 1992a, 1992b) and Bell (1992) give landscape recommendations for each silvicultural system. The course to reach an acceptable solution will be by the recognition and application of good design standards. Critical areas in the landscape, such as along public access routes and on hilltops and skylines may need special attention to avoid negative and intrusive effects.

Landscape will not be the only consideration affecting the choice of silvicultural system. The use of alternatives to clear cutting will not necessarily produce an acceptable solution in the landscape, and basic principles should be applied at the outset of the design process. Woods and forests should be viewed as an element in the wider landscape and should be designed as an integral part of it, to respect landscape character. Improvements to poorly designed woods and forests will not be brought about by choice of silvicultural system alone. In their *Lowland landscape guidelines* the Forestry Commission (1992b) give detailed advice on the visual aspects of various options for felling and regeneration.

Impact on nature conservation

Presence of wildlife in its many forms is a major attribute to woods and forests. Silvicultural systems have a great impact on mammals, reptiles, butterflies, insects, birds and plants. Protecting sensitive habitat areas is an important part of maintaining diversity. Some ecologists, as well as some discerning lay people, have considered uniform even-aged woods to be of lower conservation value than those with an uneven-aged diverse structure (Peterken, 1981). While the latter offer the desired permanence and diverse habitat, uniform even-aged forest under the extensive *clear cutting system* can be less conducive to certain types of wildlife. Stands managed under *shelterwood systems* likewise can be inadequate. *Coppice* and *coppice with standards* can encourage a rich woodland fauna and flora, depending on the age of the trees. Being deciduous, they can be dull and gloomy in winter, but in spring the field layer of flowering plants can be very rich particularly with bluebells, wood anemones, oxlips and celandines. The practice of coppicing develops a distinctive flora and fauna; with the repeated cycle of sunlight and dense shade providing ideal conditions for both sun-loving and shade-tolerant species. There is a regular cycling of stored seed banks of herbs.

The *single tree selection system* is recommended for its continuity of habitat conditions. A possible disadvantage for nature conservation is the lack of diversity. However, the multistoried diverse structure is highly desirable for some species of breeding birds, and within any stand there will be small-scale spatial variations in shading and hence of flora and shrub layer communities. The intimate mixing of old and young trees, and the continuous woodland conditions, are ideal for sustaining a diverse epiphytic flora. In *group systems*, wildlife conservation is favoured by two attributes of a degree of continuity of forest cover and diversity of structure and species. In all systems, the understorey, as well as shrubs, herbs and field layer—particularly brambles—can lessen disturbance to wildlife when it provides safe cover for mammals and helps to deter people and dogs straying too far from paths.

The use of natural regeneration brings many wildlife conservation benefits, favouring species already on the site, tending to generate mixed stands, and creating a more diverse structure than plantations. The selection, group shelterwood, and coppice systems are increasingly being appreciated by conservationists. *Forest nature conservation guidelines*

(Forestry Commission, 1990) is a highly beneficial publication. The relevant treatment of ancient and semi-natural woodlands, which contribute in a significant way to the welfare of wildlife, is discussed in the *Guidelines for the management of broadleaved woodlands* and *The management of semi-natural woodlands* (Forestry Commission, 1985, 1994).

Effect on recreational potential

Woods and forests are a major asset for outdoor recreation, their importance depending on extent, age, structure, species mix, internal visual quality, accessibility, nearness to urban areas, and tourism in the locality (Broadhurst, 1993). Public interest in forest recreation has built up over the last few decades and will continue. Access must ensure that it is compatible with environmental and wildlife protection and the interests of all users of the forest. The most popular and compatible forms are those described as informal, that is, they depend for their appeal on natural factors. Extensive areas of clear cutting are significantly disliked. Silvicultural systems based on at least a degree of permanence of parts of the upper canopy and with varied height and structure of stand appear to find most favour. Despite all the foregoing, some individuals prefer open access to forest using a clear cutting system rather than being restricted to forest using alternative systems; their highest priority being open access. Evaluation of recreation has been undertaken by Benson and Willis (1992) and useful consideration given to the subject by Ruffell and Hanley (1993). Management for recreation is discussed by Hart (1991) and Hummel (1992). *Forest recreation guidelines* (Forestry Commission, 1992a) provides some essential reading. In general any silvicultural system which gives due attention to landscape and nature conservation is also likely to provide acceptable conditions for recreation potential.

Conclusions on the influence of environmental factors

1. *Effect of wind.* The wind input into a silvicultural system is dependent upon the region in which it is located and local topography. As the transition from one silvicultural system to another involves significant risk, windthrow should be given serious consideration in selecting appropriate sites and systems.

2. *Effect of damaging mammals.* Adequate recognition of deer behaviour and requirements are vital during conversion, with deer management being seen as part of an integrated forest design strategy. To avoid damage by grey squirrels methods of controlling populations are available and effective if properly applied.

3. *Impact on landscape, nature conservation and recreation potential.* A detailed assessment is necessary of the impact of silvicultural systems and operations. The nearer the approach to achievement of continuous forest cover, the more is the likelihood of satisfying aesthetic and environmental objectives. Although restructuring (see Chapter 5) provides an improved landscape and slightly greater diversity than the original planting, it is still generally based on the clear cutting system.

63

Chapter 8

Conclusions: resources and benefits, opportunities and recommendations

General

- Britain's woods and forests are a valuable renewable natural resource, producing timber and at the same time providing important non-wood benefits. The public are demanding that greater emphasis be placed on the latter in forest management. There is growing concern to create 'near to nature' forest, and advocation of an extension of silvicultural systems giving continuous forest cover. This has led to renewed interest in irregular uneven-aged forest, as opposed to the extensive clear cutting system normally adopted in larger woods and forests in Britain. The former is claimed to achieve 'non-wood' benefits better than uniform even-aged forest. Debate continues as to the scale and kind of adjustment desired to meet the demands for more beautiful, more varied, more diversified and more wildlife-rich woods and forests.

- A forester skilled in operating the clear cutting system may not be the most suited to the slower pace of regeneration and smaller scale of the alternative systems, or be best prepared for some of the setbacks which may occur when attempting conversion from even-aged to irregular systems of management. The forester must be innovative, patient and opportunistic in gaining silvicultural and management advantages. If such attributes are not provided continually the new stands may soon revert to a uniform canopy.

- A key factor in the success of examples of irregular forestry in Britain, notably at Weasenham, has been continuity of ownership and management. Large areas of forest are managed by the State and private companies who frequently transfer personnel to provide breadth of experience and flexibility. Such movement of staff is not conducive to developing the skills for conversion to irregular forestry, or maintaining such systems. Costs of management of irregular forestry are thought to be high; but this is not so if a value is placed on *permanent* amenity, recreation and the provision of habitat for wildlife. (Irregular forestry and the selection systems are clearly the better providers of these benefits.)

- There is a need for thought to accommodate changes to irregular systems in the economics of forest management. There will be financial gains and losses between even-aged and irregular systems especially during the conversion phase; the values of the relevant costs and benefits are variable and uncertain. More research is required to decide if a fully convincing *economic* case can be made for irregular systems to be more widely used. Such systems do appear to be worth while and affordable on smaller areas for certain objectives of high multi-purpose use, and sometimes in sheltered upland sites with a moderate extent of well-drained soils. There is a strong case for them in areas of high recreational use.

- As forest conditions on the Continent are often different to those in Britain, the alternative systems should not be an exact model for Britain; they should be used intelligently as useful guides, as in many of the examples cited in this Bulletin. However, more use of natural regeneration is justified, especially with broadleaves in lowland Britain and similarly with birch and Scots pine on northern and eastern heaths, Douglas fir in sheltered locations, and Sitka spruce in uplands. Suitable systems (shelterwood uniform and shelterwood group) and mosaics of small patch clear cutting which are naturally regenerated would greatly soften the impact of the restocking stage on conservation and landscape. These systems can be applied with suitable variation to broadleaves, conifers and mixed woods, and adapted to shade-bearers and light-demanders.

Experience in Britain

- Several examples of conversion to alternative systems or adaptations of them are available for study. Some have reached a halfway stage, some are showing promise, but it may be too soon to be certain that the desired objectives will always be fully attained. Regrettably, adequate records are lacking (exceptions are the Ipsden Estate and Glentress). Foresters should make themselves more familiar with these demonstrations and other examples should be introduced and research undertaken.

- Notable examples of the group shelterwood system exist in the lowlands involving natural regeneration, both conifer and broadleaved. In the uplands, use of natural regeneration has been less significant, and then mainly of Scots pine or Sitka spruce but there are relatively small scale examples of western hemlock (Kyloe), Douglas fir (Coed y Brenin, The Hermitage, Craigvinean and Faskally), and Sitka spruce, Norway spruce and larch (Glentress). The longer each system has been employed, the more dependable natural regeneration has become as the means of restocking.

- The examples in Britain have taught several lessons, significantly:

1. Failures have occurred through (a) group clearings being too small, (b) mixtures over-complex, (c) inadequate control of deer (sometimes in the interests of sporting) and grey squirrels, and (d) lack of appreciation of need for lateral light and for sustained action to develop the groups (e.g. 'relief' thinning on their edges).

2. Foresters can be unsuccessful if they (a) begin conversion too late, (b) wait too long for natural regeneration and unduly delay planting, and (c) allow expanding group regeneration to seed the whole stand, and, by not reserving groups of large sized trees, risk reversion to even-aged structure; continual attention is essential.

3. Adequate access is required for the frequent small scale cutting and tending operations needed to operate the systems.

4. Deer, grey squirrels, hares and rabbits can seriously damage all systems. A combination of effective fencing and control of animal numbers is essential.

5. Conversion to, and management of, uneven-aged systems can have some problems and can generate additional costs.

6. There has to be investment in staff training and continuity of staff is highly desirable. Frequent changes of ownership and objectives are adverse.

Opportunities in Britain

- It is possible to achieve an uneven-aged structure on a range of sites in Britain (Paterson, 1990) using the shade-tolerant species that can be grown here and which regenerate satisfactorily on certain site types. Britain's woods and forests, especially in the uplands, are very varied in land form, climate, soil type, vegetation type and tree species mix: a variety encouraging different approaches to stand structure and diversification. As a result of its multi-purpose objectives, Forest Enterprise is identifying parts of its forest to be managed as permanent structures.

- There will be differences between the type of irregular systems and management appropriate for (a) extensive forests on upland and lowland heaths chiefly comprising monocultures of uniform even-aged conifers, and (b) traditional small broadleaved or mixed species stands in the lowlands. In the first case, where most forests have been developed as even-aged plantations on a large scale, foresters will continue to mainly use simple but less extensive methods, e.g. shelterwood systems as at Windsor Forest. By contrast, in the more populated lowlands, foresters must seek an intimate balance between many objectives, i.e. commercial, amenity, conservation and field sport. This may require more intensive silviculture and management, and may be more appropriate for systems such as group selection or single tree selection.

- Helpfully, there is already some unevenness of structure/development stage among the post-1950 growing-stock in the uplands because of planting dates, species differences, provenance differences, variations in site quality, yield class, 'check' and sporadic windthrow.

- Furthermore, advantage can be taken of the ameliorated microclimate and improved site conditions created by the extensive productive, mainly coniferous, plantations; these conditions now permit the regeneration of a wider choice of species, provided that high standards of protection from browsing animals are rigorously pursued. Moreover, the mid-rotation stands provide opportunities to convert some of them from a uniform to a diverse structure, which may lead to 'semi-permanent' or continuous forest cover.

- On windswept upland sites, the clear cutting silvicultural system, despite its drawbacks to aesthetic and conservation interests, remains the most effective system suitable for the light-demanding species, mainly Sitka spruce, extensively planted to produce timber at competitive prices. Opportunities for irregular forestry are constrained in these situations by high windthrow hazard class, but

patch clear cutting and restocking, or restructuring, are procedures which can help to diversify even-aged structure to meet multiple objectives. There may be scope for using group or wedge shelterwood systems and natural regeneration (e.g. in areas of WHC 4) in the conversion of these plantations.

- In the uplands, there are areas with well-drained soils suitable for some form of alternative to the clear cutting system, for example shelterwood systems on low windthrow hazard class sites (WHC 1 and 2), or strip or wedge systems on higher wind hazard sites (WHC 3 and 4). It is essential to match appropriate silvicultural systems with sites of different windthrow hazard class (see Table 7.1). Detailed advice on this point is given by Paterson (1990): see Table 8.1.

- In the lowlands, conversion to group selection or shelterwood systems could be appropriate for broadleaved and mixed stands, especially in sensitive locations, mainly by traditional private sector woodland owners who appreciate and desire the relevant benefits. The development of many variants can be expected. There is also ample opportunity for use of the uniform shelterwood system in plantation pinewoods, particularly on the heaths and breckland of lowland England. Although the system results in even-aged stands, it is a much more environmentally acceptable method than clear cutting during the regeneration stage.

- Only where significantly advanced uneven-aged diverse structure is available will attempts be undertaken to create the 'true' single tree selection system, which needs fertile soils, sheltered sites, a higher intensity of access for extraction and a higher proportion of shade-bearers.

- In conifers, Paterson (1990) considers that about 25% of existing upland conifer plantations, located mainly on brown earths, podzols and ironpan soils, are likely to be suitable for conversion to alternative systems. (There will be additional potential following an extension of conifer forests 'down-the-hill' to better soils and site conditions.) Quine (1991) appears to support Paterson's view as

Table 8.1 Possible silvicultural systems for various site groups in conifer upland forests. (*Source: Paterson, 1990, amended*)

Site group	Topex	Wind zone	WHC	Species before felling	Species after felling	Possible silvicultural system	Coupe size strip width	Dominant type of regeneration	Period of regeneration of coupe
BE	71-100	<5	1	Douglas fir	Douglas fir	Irregular shelterwood	0.2 ha	N	20-25
	71-100	<5	1	Larch	Larch	Strip regeneration	35 m x S	N + A	5-10
	71-100	<5	1/2	Larch	Douglas fir, western hemlock	Uniform shelterwood or group shelterwood	2-5 ha	A underplant	10
	41-70	<10	3	Norway spruce, Sitka spruce	Pacific fir	Leeward strip	25 m x S	A + N	8-10
PZ	28-40	1-5	2	Scots pine	Douglas fir, western hemlock	Uniform shelterwood or group shelterwood	2-5 ha	A underplant + N(SP)	10
IPS	20-22	1-5	3	Scots pine	Douglas fir, western hemlock	Uniform shelterwood or group shelterwood	10-20 ha	A underplant	10
SWG	25-27	1-5	3	Norway spruce	Sitka spruce, Norway spruce	Wedge or group shelterwood	2 ha lateral expansion	N + A	5 progressive
	25-27	1-5	4	Sitka spruce	Sitka spruce	Leeward strip	20 m x S	N + A	5 progressive
PG	10-15	1-5	5	Sitka spruce	Sitka spruce	Patch clear cutting	10-15 ha	A + N	3-5
	10-15	5-9	6	Sitka spruce	Sitka spruce, lodgepole pine	Patch clear cutting	10-15 ha	A + N	3-5
PIPS/PG/PT	18-19	5-10	4/5	Sitka spruce, lodgepole pine, Japanese larch	Sitka spruce, larch, Noble fir	Patch clear cutting	2-5 ha	A + N	5
PT	18-19	5-10	5	Sitka spruce, lodgepole pine,	Sitka spruce, western red cedar	Patch clear cutting	?	N + A	5-8

Key

BE: brown earth, PZ: podzol, IPS: ironpan soil, SWG: surface-water gley non-peaty, PG: peaty gley, PIPS: peaty ironpan soil, PT: peat.
A: planting, N: natural regeneration, S: length of strip variable.

there are many sites in the lower windthrow hazard classes and on better soils where endemic damage from normal winter storms will only rarely be experienced.

- Broadleaved species in the lowlands offer much scope for application of diverse structure systems, especially with the aid of natural regeneration, and can provide or enhance non-wood benefits. Notable examples have been recorded in Chapters 3 and 4.

Variants of group selection can be applied on sites with soils capable of supporting good growth of oak, beech, ash, wild cherry, sycamore and birch. The windthrow hazard needs generally to be low. Most species can be accommodated by adjusting the size of the groups in the range of 0.3-1.0 ha. Small groups will accommodate beech, medium size sycamore and ash, and large size oak and birch. Rabbits, hares, grey squirrels and deer must be controlled. Such potential will appeal to owners whose commitment to amenity, sporting and public recreation is strong. Shelterwood systems using broadleaves need to be on deep soils and on wind-stable sites of low risk windthrow hazard (WHC 1 and 2). They can be successful with oak, beech, ash, sycamore and birch. The single tree selection system, when using broadleaves, is difficult to achieve, though at one time successful at Rossie Priory. In all such systems using broadleaves, the benefits of an understorey (distinct from a young crop) are important (Everard, 1985; Reade, 1991), suppressing branches and epicormic shoots on the stems of favoured trees, and protecting the soil.

Conversion

- To create, by planting groups, a stand to be managed under the selection system or under any other irregular system, would take many decades and generate prohibitive costs. The creation of group selection and shelterwood systems from middle-aged regular stands on well-drained soils is a better approach. It is necessary to use heavy crown thinning in the run up to regeneration. However, irregular structure is also achiev-

able for specific objectives by an earlier conversion of existing pole-stage/mid-rotation stands (especially of seedbearing age) on suitable sites in appropriate locations, taking a longer time but achieving a wider range of size classes. It entails some sacrificed revenue from premature felling.

- The period of conversion for conifers should not exceed 30 years because of cost and the need for continuity of management; some foresters suggest this is too short, and recommend 40-50 years. Others point out that pine and larch can easily stand for 90-120 years, and broadleaves 120-140 years. If for some reason conversion is delayed, it is generally because some difficulty has appeared that was not foreseen at the outset.

- It is probably unrealistic to attempt complex conversions unless conditions of ownership, forest management, existing growing stock, and site are very favourable. Although carefully constructed conversion schemes (e.g. the Bradford-Hutt Plan at Tavistock) are commendable, more simple procedures have also proved successful. It is to be expected that the majority of conversions will rarely exceed 100 ha, and that rotations, whether nominal or formal, will be in the range of 80 to 120 years for broadleaves, 50 to 90 years for pine and larch and 50 to 70 years for other conifers. However, rotations over 80 years may not be financially viable.

- Associated interests or activities are needed to provide income which accrues directly or indirectly to the irregular forest. Particularly in the private sector, fine landscape, beautiful dwellings, an historic monument, or outstanding recreational or wildlife features should generally be present to enhance potential income or justify in some other way the increased efforts devoted to irregular forest.

- During the period when an area with its existing stands is being converted to a new system, particularly for continuous cover, the forester must concentrate on restraining costs because benefits are likely to be few in the early years. The best that can be hoped for is that income and expenditure are kept in balance. When the structure of the whole forest takes shape the benefits will increase, and at this stage it will be possible to appraise the financial conditions needed to make the new system permanent. Until that stage is reached, estimates of the long-term costs and benefits are likely to be unrealistic. The work done during conversion will not be wasted: this is a suitable point in time at which to consider whether the case remains strong for continuation with the proposed system.

- When the conversion is approximately 40% complete, income from the forest should be significant: based on the fact that the main sources of income from the forest itself will arise from thinnings and large diameter fellings, and from other charged-for goods and services including recreation.

- The timber and the non-wood values of the uneven-aged shelterwood, single tree selection and group selection systems appear to be comparable. The experience gained so far is greatest with the group selection and group shelterwood systems, which have worked well both in the less exposed uplands and the lowlands, and can accommodate the requirements of a wide range of species, from light-demanding to shade-enduring. The appearance of woods and forests run on these systems in Britain cannot be claimed as equal to Continental stands because they have been developed under different conditions.

- It appears probable that a good route to uneven-aged forest is through periodic underplanting (plus natural seeding) of parts of heavily thinned mid pole-stage stands (e.g. larch, Scots pine) to produce multi-storied high forest. A good structure for the group selection system consists of a mosaic of even-aged stands of varying species, ages and extents (this is the essence of Garfitt's approach; likewise at Longleat).

Summary of benefits of alternative systems

- Uneven-aged systems are claimed to have benefits which could make them more important for Britain in future. The following environmental and silvicultural benefits are claimed as more readily obtained, compared with the clear cutting system. (They chiefly refer to the group selection and single tree selection systems and to conifers in the uplands.)

Environmental benefits

1. Less change in internal and external landscape and a more natural and diverse appearance which is better habitat for plants, animals, birds and other wildlife, and often a greater variety of them. Pleasant surroundings for field sport and recreation.

2. Site productivity improved as a result of soil conservation and maintenance of stability of the ecosystem. Soil temperatures increased, prolonging growth and biological activity. Soil protection against erosion, particularly on steep slopes. Efficient use of light through absorption by a number of photosynthetically active canopy layers, increasing the productivity. A stable ground water regime, with no sudden movement of sediments, and no significant change in flow rate and water quality.

Silvicultural benefits

1. When regenerating by planting, the lower concentration of fresh felled stumps may limit the population of pine weevil and black pine beetle, thus reducing damage to the young plants. Damage by insects and disease is theoretically reduced, but managerial practices are most important in determining the level of damage.

2. Where natural regeneration is adequate, there is no need for conventional ground preparation, planting and beating up; and the cost of weeding can be reduced (although respacing and cleaning are necessary).

3. Tree stability is improved and there is less risk of snowbreak. The relationship between stand structure and wind stability depends largely on the soil type, ground preparation, the thinning regime and the manner in which 'forest edge' is exposed and the stand prepared for it. Anchorage characteristics are probably improved by the rougher canopy of diverse structure stressing trees and reducing height/diameter ratio compared with even-aged.

4. The claim that irregular forestry leads to a reduced fire risk is difficult to verify as most Continental systems are used in areas of low fire risk.

5. Deer population may be on a more stable and predictable level, due to an absence of the otherwise typical peaks and troughs arising from violent changes in browse and cover. Control may be easier as a result of less disturbance of the habitat and range. However, appropriate control is essential over the whole area.

Management economics of alternative systems

- Conversion of even-aged to uneven-aged systems may involve loss in timber revenue through premature felling or deferred income from prolonged retention, or both. Relevant factors include:

1. Timber yield: whereas in the clear cutting system, conventionally there is a periodic series of thinnings from approximately age 20-30 in conifers, in selection forest there is usually a more consistent and higher average tree size harvested, and hence of higher value, but there is a wide assortment range and difficulties with many species in a batch of produce. It is difficult to calculate the potential yield of timber for uneven-aged stands, without relevant management models but little difference in gross yield appears likely.

2. Timber quality: the canopy, being more open contains a greater number of trees of dominant, large diameter category, usually of higher value than many of those in the clear cutting system. However, this may be offset by the proportion of timber produced from the upper part of large dominants and edge of group trees which are growing free of competition and therefore producing a higher degree of knotty timber.

3. Harvesting: this may be scattered leading to higher cost operations, and constraints on the use of machinery; and supervision needs to be more intensive. Costs per cubic metre tend to fall considerably as trees increase in size; the mean volume of trees removed from some forms of uneven-aged forest (in particular, selection forest) is likely to be greater than that of trees grown under an even-aged system. Sorting of mixed size assortments and species is more costly.

4. Profitability: much depends on species and site conditions and the value attributed to non-wood benefits. Some factors may make significant contributions to profitability. Management of uneven-aged systems (especially where flora and fauna are important along with timber production) generally requires a high level of skills, and adequate knowledge of structure of stands to ascertain and undertake timely silvicultural treatment. There may be a regular cash flow in uneven-aged forests from sustained yield of marketable timber. However, it is wrong to suggest that uneven-aged structure on a large scale is the sole route to sustained income; this could be attained by a collection of even-aged stands giving a *normal* forest.

Some present day management, financial and industrial factors obstruct the use of alternative silvicultural systems, for example instability of ownership/supervision, emphasis on short-term income, and contracted commitments to supply to the small roundwood market, and even the grant-aid structure.

- The clear cutting and replant system will remain appropriate in many places, but there will be an increasing use of alternative silvicultural systems, especially in areas which are visually and biologically sensitive and where the risk of windthrow is not too great.

Postscript

The conversion of unmanaged or derelect woodland, and of even-aged plantations, to a more uneven-aged forest, often of several species, has been described in this Bulletin from 44 different sites in England, Wales and Scotland. The silvicultural systems used in 15 cases are uniform or group shelterwood, in 17 cases group selection, in 4 cases single tree selection, and in 8 cases various other systems including the technique called 'restructuring'. The pioneer conversion of one stand (New Wood, Weasenham Estate) is virtually complete; that of several others is at a halfway stage or slightly more advanced; while the conversion of the remainder began more recently.

The sustained effort of owners and their foresters during several decades has produced many of the desired ends:

- Natural regeneration is often present.

- The growing-stock contains trees of good growth and quality.

- The different age or size classes essential to sustained yield are developing.

- The external and internal appearance of the stands is pleasing.

In short, the examples show the expected benefits of careful silviculture with a clear environmental objective. They are modest attempts to create 'forests with true structure and diversity that more accurately mimic natural and sustainable [forest] ecosystems' (Whitfield, 1993).

There are uncertainties that must still be resolved. The lack of information concerning volume increment and value of the benefits obtained from uneven-aged stands in Britain, and of the costs of conversion to gain the desired benefits, makes the collection and analysis of such information essential. Recommendations are made for this in Appendix 3.

Finally, appreciation is recorded to the owners and foresters who have explored for everyone's benefit the idea of continuous cover forestry in Britain during the past 40 years.

REFERENCES

Aldhous, J.R. (1981). Beech in Wessex – a perspective on present health and silviculture. *Forestry* **54**, 197-210.

Anderson, M.L. (1930). A new system of planting. *Scottish Forestry* **44**, 78-87.

Anderson, M.L. (1931). Planting in dense groups spaced at intervals. *Quarterly Journal of Forestry* **25**, 312-316.

Anderson, M.L. (1951). Spaced group planting and irregularity of stand structure. *Empire Forestry Review* **30**, 328-341.

Anderson, M.L. (1953). Plea for the adoption of the standing control or check in woodland management. *Scottish Forestry* **7**, 38-47.

Anderson, M.L. (1960). Norway spruce–silver fir–beech mixed selection forest. *Scottish Forestry* **14**, 328-341.

Anderson, M.L. (1967). *A history of Scottish forestry*. Nelson, London.

Bell, S. (1992). Landscape design for irregular forestry. *Continuous Cover Forestry Newsletter* **2**, 6-7.

Benezit, J.J. (1991). Soils and natural regeneration in Normandy. *Quarterly Journal of Forestry* **85**, 30-36.

Benson, J.F. and Willis, K.G. (1992). *Valuing informal recreation on the Forestry Commission estate*. Forestry Commission Bulletin 104. HMSO, London.

Biolley, H. (1920). *The planning of managed forests by the experimental method and especially the check method*. Translated by M. L. Anderson (1954). The Schrivener Press, Oxford.

Blyth, J. (1986). Edinburgh University experimental area, Glentress Forest. Internal Report, Department of Forestry and Natural Resources, University of Edinburgh.

Blyth, J. and Malcolm, D.C. (1988). *The development of a transformation to irregular forest: 35 years' experience at the Glentress Trial Area*. O.F.I. Occasional Paper No. 37. Oxford Forestry Institute, Oxford, 33-41.

Bourne, R. (1945). The neglect of natural regeneration. *Forestry* **19** 33-40.

Bourne, R. (1951). A fallacy in the theory of growing stock. *Forestry* **24**, 6-18.

Bradford, Lord (1981). An experiment in irregular forestry. *Y Coedwigr* **33**, 1, 6-18.

Broadhurst, R. (1993). Forests, woodlands and people's preferences. *Countryside Recreation Network News* No. 1, 6-7.

Brown, J.M.B. (1953). *Studies on British beechwoods*. Forestry Commission Bulletin 20. HMSO, London.

Buckley, G.P. (ed.) (1992). *Ecology and management of coppice woodlands*. Chapman & Hall, London.

Cawdor, Lord (1985). Historical notes on management (of Cawdor Wood). Cawdor Archives.

Chilterns Standing Conference (1971). *A plan for the Chilterns*. Buckinghamshire County Council, Aylesbury, Bucks.

Chilterns Standing Conference (1988). *A plan for the Chilterns woodlands policy*. Buckinghamshire County Council, Aylesbury, Bucks.

Chilterns Standing Conference (1993). *Introduction to the management of small woods in the Chilterns*. Buckinghamshire County Council, Aylesbury, Bucks.

Crowe, S. (1978). *The landscape of forests and woods*. Forestry Commission Booklet 44. HMSO, London.

Crowther, R.E. and Evans, J. (1986). *Coppice*. Forestry Commission Leaflet 83 (second edition). HMSO, London.

Edwards, I.D. (1981). The conservation of the Glen Tanar native pinewoods, near Aboyne, Aberdeenshire. *Scottish Forestry* **35**, 173-178.

Evans, J. (1984). *Silviculture of broadleaved woodland*. Forestry Commission Bulletin 62. HMSO, London.

Evans, J. (1988). *Natural regeneration of broadleaves*. Forestry Commission Bulletin 78. HMSO, London.

Everard, J. (1985). *Management of broadleaved forests in Western Europe*. Forestry Commission, Edinburgh.

Everard, J. (1992). Natural regeneration of oak in Normandy. *Quarterly Journal of Forestry* **86,** 173-180.

Fairbairn, W.A. (1963). Some observations on group regeneration. *Forestry* **36**, 113-123.

Farmer, R. (1991). Achieving multi-benefits in upland forestry. ICF Wales and Marches Regional Group Discussion, Llandrindod Wells, 29 November 1991.

Forestry Commission (1985). *Guidelines for the management of broadleaved woodland.* Forestry Commission, Edinburgh.

Forestry Commission (1990). *Forest nature conservation guidelines.* HMSO, London.

Forestry Commission (1991). *Community woodland design guidelines.* HMSO, London.

Forestry Commission (1992a). *Forest recreation guidelines.* HMSO, London.

Forestry Commission (1992b). *Lowland landscape guidelines.* HMSO, London.

Forestry Commission (1994a). *Forest landscape design guidelines*, 2nd edition. HMSO, London.

Forestry Commission (1994b). *The management of semi-natural woodlands.* Forestry Practice Guides 1-8. Forestry Commission, Edinburgh.

Garfitt, J.E. (1953). The rehabilitation of devastated woodlands. *Forestry* **26**, 28-32.

Garfitt, J.E. (1963). Treatment of natural regeneration. *Forestry* **36**, 109-112.

Garfitt, J.E. (1966). Edge-effect. *Forestry* **39**, 189-190.

Garfitt, J.E. (1977). Irregular forestry in the service of amenity. *Quarterly Journal of Forestry* **71**, 82-85.

Garfitt, J.E. (1979). The importance of brashing. *Quarterly Journal of Forestry* **73**, 153-154.

Garfitt, J.E. (1980). Treatment of natural regeneration and young broadleaved crops. *Quarterly Journal of Forestry* **74**, 236-239.

Garfitt, J.E. (1984). The group selection system. *Quarterly Journal of Forestry* **78**, 155-158.

Garfitt, J.E. (1987). Yield control of irregular woodlands. *Quarterly Journal of Forestry* **81**, 181-184.

Garfitt, J.E. (1988). *Irregular systems of silviculture for broadleaves and mixed crops: do they work in an English context?* O.F.I. Occasional Paper No. 37. Oxford Forestry Institute, Oxford, 47-51.

Garfitt, J.E. (1995). *Natural management of woods: continuous cover forestry.* Research Studies Press Ltd, Taunton.

Garthwaite, P.F. (1972). Windsor Forest. Internal Report to the Nature Conservancy Council (unpublished).

Gibson, W.N. (1953). Exotic conifers and their importance to forestry in Northern Ireland and the West of Scotland. *Scottish Forestry* **7**, 3-10.

Gill, R.M.A. (1992). A review of damage by mammals in north temperate forests. 3: Impact on trees and forests. *Forestry* **65**, 363-88.

Goss, D.W. (1992). The silviculture of oak in Scotland. *Scottish Forestry* **46**, 212-222.

Greig, D.A. (1990). The lowland pine forests of England and Wales. In *Silvicultural systems*, ed. P. Gordon. Proceedings of a Discussion Meeting, University of York 6-8 April. Institute of Chartered Foresters, Edinburgh, 139-146.

Hart, C.E. (1966). *Royal forest: A history of Dean's Woods as producers of timber.* Clarendon Press, Oxford.

Hart, C.E. (1991). *Practical forestry for the agent and surveyor*, 3rd edition. Alan Sutton Publishing, Stroud.

Helliwell, D.R. (1982). *Options in forestry.* Packard, Chichester.

Helliwell, D.R. (1985). The need for an experimental study of different silvicultural systems. *Scottish Forestry*, **39**, 9-12.

Hibberd, B.G. (1985). Restructuring of plantations in Kielder forest district. *Forestry* **58**, 119-129.

Hiley, W.E. (1953). Irregular forestry. *Quarterly Journal of Forestry* **47**, 231-237.

Hiley, W.E. (1956). Underplanting of Japanese larch. *Quarterly Journal of Forestry* **50**, 189-196.

Hiley, W.E. (1959). Two-storied high forest. *Forestry* **32**, 113-116.

Hiley, W.E. (1964). *A forestry venture.* Faber and Faber, London.

Hiley, W.E. (1967). *Woodland management*, 2nd edition. Faber and Faber, London.

Hill-Tout, P. (1990). Deer and restocking - factors influencing the choice of silvicultural system. In *Silvicultural systems*, ed. P. Gordon. Proceedings of a Discussion Meeting, University of York 6-8 April. Institute of Chartered Foresters, Edinburgh, 82-84.

Howell, B.N., Harley, R.M., White, R.D.F. and Lamb, R.G.M. (1983). The Dartington story, II. *Quarterly Journal of Forestry* **77**, 5-16.

Hummel, F.C. (1992). Aspects of forest recreation in western Europe. *Forestry* **65**, 237-251.

Hutt, P. and Watkins, K. (1971). The Bradford plan for continuous forest cover. *Journal of the Devon Trust for Nature Conservation* **3**, 69-74.

James, N. D. G. (1981). *A history of English forestry*. Basil Blackwell, Oxford.

Jobling, J. and Pearce, M.L. (1977). *Free growth of oak*. Forestry Commission Forest Record 113. HMSO, London.

Johnston, D.R. (1978). Irregularity in British forestry. *Forestry* **51**, 163-169.

Johnston, D.R., Grayson, A.J. and Bradley, R.T. (1967). *Forest planning*. Faber and Faber, London.

Jones, E.W. (1952). *Silvicultural systems,* 2nd edition. Clarendon Press, Oxford.

Joslin, A. (1982). Management of broadleaves in the Forest of Dean, with special reference to regeneration. In *Broadleaves in Britain: future management and research*, eds D.C. Malcolm, J. Evans, and P.N. Edwards. Institute of Chartered Foresters, Edinburgh, 53-60.

Kerr, G. and Evans, J. (1993). *Growing broadleaves for timber.* Forestry Commission Handbook 9. HMSO, London.

Knüchel, H. (1953). *Planning and control in the managed forest*. Translated by M.L. Anderson. Oliver and Boyd, Edinburgh.

Köstler, J. (1956). *Silviculture*. Translated by M.L. Anderson. Oliver and Boyd, Edinburgh.

Lorrain-Smith, R. (1986). Economic aspects of uneven-aged forestry. *Proceedings of the discussion group on uneven-aged silviculture*. Report of a Meeting, Pershore, 29 October 1986. (Obtainable from D.R. Helliwell, Yokecliffe House, West End, Wirksworth, Derbyshire DE4 4EG.)

Low, A.J. (ed.) (1985). *Guide to upland restocking practice*. Forestry Commission Leaflet 84. HMSO, London.

Low, A.J. (1988). Scarification as an aid to natural regeneration in the Glen Tanar native pinewood. *Scottish Forestry* **42**, 15-20.

Lucas, O.W.R. (1991). *The design of forest landscapes*. Oxford University Press, Oxford.

McIntosh, E. (1990). Landscape considerations for various silvicultural systems in the U.K. In *Silvicultural systems*, ed. P. Gordon. Proceedings of a Discussion Meeting, University of York 6-8 April. Institute of Chartered Foresters, Edinburgh, 88-110.

McIntosh, R. (1991). Planning for the second rotation. In *Forestry practice,* ed. B.G. Hibberd. Forestry Commission Handbook 6. HMSO, London, 211-222.

McNeill, J.D. and Thompson, D.A. (1982). Natural regeneration of Sitka spruce in the forest of Ae. *Scottish Forestry* **36**, 269-282.

Malcolm, D.C. (1971). Corrour management trial. *Scottish Forestry* **25**, 262-269.

Malcolm, D.C. (1992). The development of a transformation from even-aged plantations to an irregularly-structured forest. Report to the Scottish Forestry Trust. School of Forestry, Institute of Ecology and Resource Management, University of Edinburgh.

Matthews, J.D. (1990). The evolution of silvicultural systems in western and central Europe. In *Silvicultural systems*, ed. P. Gordon. Proceedings of a Discussion Meeting, University of York 6-8 April. Institute of Chartered Foresters, Edinburgh, 1-19.

Matthews, J.D. (1963). Factors affecting the production of seed of forest trees. *Forestry Abstracts* **24**, i-xiii.

Matthews, J.D. (1986). The history and status of uneven-aged forestry in Europe and Britain. *Proceedings of the discussion group on uneven-aged silviculture*. Report of a Meeting, Pershore, 29 October 1986, 3-16. (Obtainable from D.R. Helliwell, Yokecliffe House, West End, Wirksworth, Derbyshire DE4 4EG.)

Matthews, J.D. (1989, 1992). *Silvicultural systems,* 2nd edition. Clarendon Press, Oxford.

Matthews, J.D. (1991). Silvicultural systems for the 1990s. ICF Wales and Marches Regional Group Discussion, Llandrindod Wells, 29 November 1991.

Miegroet, M. van (1962). The silvicultural treatment of small woodlands. *Bulletin de la Société Royale Forestière de Belgique* **69**, 437-456.

Miller, H.G. and Ross, I. (1990). Management and silviculture of the forests of Deeside. In *Silvicultural systems*, ed. P. Gordon. Proceedings of a Discussion Meeting, University of York 6-8 April. Institute of Chartered Foresters, Edinburgh.

Miller, K.F. (1985). *Windthrow hazard classification*. Forestry Commission Leaflet 85. HMSO, London.

Neustein, S.A. (1964). Windthrow on the margins of various sizes of felling area. *Forestry Commission Report on Forest Research 1964*. HMSO, London, 166-171.

Neustein, S.A. (1970). In *Forestry Commission Report on Forest Research 1970*. HMSO, London.

Newton, J.P. (1986). The suitability of irregular forestry for special areas in Britain - a preliminary study. Unpublished thesis, University of Edinburgh.

Osmaston, F.C. (1968). *The management of forests*. Allen and Unwin, London.

Paterson, D.B. (1953). A study in stand structure and management of irregular forests. Thesis. University of Edinburgh.

Paterson, D.B. (1958). *A study in stand structure and management of irregular forests*. Bulletin 5. Forestry Department, University of Edinburgh.

Paterson, D.B. (1990). The potential to apply different silvicultural systems to upland British forests, predominantly of Sitka spruce. In *Silvicultural systems*, ed. P. Gordon. Proceedings of a Discussion Meeting, University of York 6-8 April. Institute of Chartered Foresters, Edinburgh, 120-138.

Penistan, M.J. (1952). The alternative to extensive regular clear felling. *Scottish Forestry* 6.

Penistan, M.J. (1960). Forestry in the Belgian uplands. *Forestry* 33, 1-7.

Penistan, M.J. (1968). The 75th anniversary of the Société Royale Forestière de Belgique. *Quarterly Journal of Forestry* 62, 304-310.

Penistan, M.J. (1974). The silviculture of beech woodland. In *The management of broadleaved woodlands*. Supplement to *Forestry* 47, 71-78.

Peterken, G.F. (1981). *Woodland conservation and management*. Chapman and Hall, London.

Peterken, G.F., Ausherman, D., Buchenau, M. and Forman, R.T.T. (1992). Old-growth conservation within British upland conifer plantations. *Journal of Forestry* 65, 127-144.

Philip, M.S. (1994). *Measuring trees and forests*, 2nd edition. CAB International, Wallingford.

Price, C. (1989). *The theory and application of forest economics*. Basil Blackwell, Oxford.

Pryor, S.N. (1985). An evaluation of silvicultural options for broadleaved woodland. DPhil Thesis, University of Oxford.

Pryor, S.N. (1990). Practical aspects of irregular silviculture for British broadleaves. In *Silvicultural systems*, ed. P. Gordon. Proceedings of a Discussion Meeting, University of York 6-8 April. Institute of Chartered Foresters, Edinburgh, 147-166.

Pryor, S.N. and Savill, P.S. (1986). *Silvicultural systems for broadleaved woodland in Britain*. O.F.I. Occasional Paper No. 32. Oxford Forestry Institute, Oxford.

Quine, C.P. (1991). Windthrow as a constraint on silviculture. ICF Wales and Marches Regional Group Discussion, Llandrindod Wells, 29 November 1991.

Quine, C.P. and Gardiner, B.A. (1992). *Incorporating the threat of windthrow into forest design plans*. Forestry Commission Research Information Note 220. Forestry Commission, Edinburgh.

Quine, C.P. and Miller, K.F. (1990). Windthrow - a factor influencing the choice of silvicultural systems. In *Silvicultural systems*, ed. P. Gordon. Proceedings of a Discussion Meeting, University of York 6-8 April 1990. Institute of Chartered Foresters, Edinburgh, 71-81.

Quine, C.P. and White, I.M.S. (1993). *Revised windiness scores for the windthrow hazard classification: the revised scoring method*. Forestry Commission Research Information Note 230. Forestry Commission, Edinburgh.

Quine, C.P. and Wright, J.A. (1993). *The effects of revised windiness scores on the calculation and distribution of windthrow hazard class*. Forestry Commission Research Information Note 231. Forestry Commission, Edinburgh.

Quine, C. P., Coutts, M., Gardiner, B. and Pyatt, G. (1995). *Forests and wind: management to minimise damage*. Bulletin 114. HMSO, London.

Rackham, O. (1980). *Ancient woodland*. Edward Arnold, London.

Ratcliffe, P.R. (1988). Protection against animals and management for game. In *Farm woodland practice*, ed. B.G. Hibberd. Forestry Commission Handbook 3. HMSO, London, 46-57.

Reade, M.G. (1957). Sustained yield from selection forest. *Quarterly Journal of Forestry* **51**, 51-62.

Reade, M.G. (1960). Lessons from Switzerland. *Quarterly Journal of Forestry* **54**, 111-126.

Reade, M.G. (1965). Natural regeneration of beech. *Quarterly Journal of Forestry* **59**, 121-131.

Reade, M.G. (1990). Chiltern enumerations. *Quarterly Journal of Forestry* **84**, 9-22.

Ruffell, R.J. and Hanley, N. (1993). *Recreational use values of woodland features*. Forestry Commission Research Information Note 229. Forestry Commission, Edinburgh.

Savill, P. S. and Evans, J. (1986). *Plantation silviculture in temperate regions*. Clarendon Press, Oxford.

Shrimpton, N.H. (1986). Studies on the economics of irregular stands. In *Proceedings of the discussion group on uneven-aged silviculture*. Report of a Meeting, Pershore, 29 October 1986. (Obtainable from D.R. Helliwell, Yokecliffe House, West End, Wirksworth, Derbyshire DE4 4EG.)

Shrimpton, N.H. (1988). *Modelling the costs of uneven-aged forest management*. O.F.I. Occasional Paper No. 37. Oxford Forestry Institute, Oxford, 42-46.

Steven, H.M. (1948). The late Mr Ray Bourne, M.A. *Forestry* **22**, 244-245.

Taylor, C.J. (1967). Management Plan for Cawdor Wood 1967-1985. Unpublished. Department of Forestry and Natural Resources, University of Edinburgh.

Tilney-Bassett, H.A.E. (1988). Forestry in the region of the Chilterns. *Forestry* **61**, 267-286.

Troup, R.S. (1928). *Silvicultural systems*. Oxford University Press, London.

Troup, R.S. (1952). *Silvicultural systems*, 2nd edition, ed. E.W. Jones. Oxford University Press, London.

Turner, G. (1959). Note relative à la transformation des pessières en station. *Bulletin de la Société Royale Forestière de Belgique* **66**, 414-420.

Waters, T.L. and Savill, P.S. (1992). Ash and sycamore regeneration and the phenomenon of their alternation. *Forestry* **65**, 417-433.

Whiteman, A. (1991). The economic justification of continuous cover forestry. Paper delivered at a Discussion Meeting of the Continuous Cover Forestry Group, Brecon 22 October 1991.

Whitfield, P. (1993). Forestry in British Columbia: a study of environmental issues. *Forestry* **67**, 103.

Whitney McIver, H. (1991). An overview of uneven-aged forestry. *Continuous Cover Forestry Newsletter* **1**, 4-5.

Whitney McIver, H., Blyth, J.F. and Malcolm, D.C. (1992). The application of group selection working in an upland forest in south Scotland [Glentress Forest]. *Scottish Forestry* **46**, 202-211.

Willis, K.G. and Garrod, G.D. (1992). Amenity value of forests in Great Britain and its impact on the internal rate of return from Forestry. *Forestry* **65**, 331-346.

Wood, R.F. (1950). Rehabilitation of devastated and derelict woodlands. *Quarterly Journal of Forestry* **44**, 5-10.

Wood, R.F., Miller, A.D.S. and Nimmo, M. (1967). *Experiments in the rehabilitation of uneconomic broadleaved woodlands*. Forestry Commission R & D Paper 51. HMSO, London.

Workman, J. (1986). Experience in the management of beech woodlands. In *Proceedings of the discussion group on uneven-aged silviculture*. Report of a Meeting, Pershore, 29

October 1986, 17-20. (Obtainable from D.R. Helliwell, Yokecliffe House, West End, Wirksworth, Derbyshire DE4 4EG.)

Worrell, R. (1991). *Trees and the Treasury – valuing forests for society*. World Wide Fund for Nature, Godalming, Surrey.

Yorke, D.M.B. (1991a). Scope for irregularity in upland coniferous forests in Britain. *Continuous Cover Forestry Group Newsletter* **1**, 5-6.

Yorke, D.M.B. (1991b). A study of regeneration and management of uneven-aged coniferous forest in central Europe and its relevance to Great Britain. Forestry Commission internal publication.

Yorke, D.M.B. (1992). Pros and cons of the 'permanent forest'. *Forestry and British Timber*, October 1992, 20, 22, 24. Amended version in *Scottish Forestry* **47**, 6-14.

Yorke, D.M.B. (1992). The management of continuous cover conifer forests – an alternative to clear felling. Continuous Cover Forestry Group.

Glossary 1

Definition of terms

Advance growth of natural regeneration Seedling growth which appears spontaneously before the planned regeneration stage in an existing stand; sometimes achieved by reducing the canopy in advance of seeding fellings.

Alternative system A silvicultural system other than that of extensive clear cutting, patch clear cutting and coppice systems.

Biodiversity The variability among living organisms and the ecosystems of which they are part. (A multi-objective forest policy should include the aims of maintaining and enhancing levels of biodiversity where appropriate in managed forests and in semi-natural woodlands. Spatial and structural diversity in forests may provide a surrogate measure of biodiversity.)

Canopy The mass of foliage and branches formed collectively by the crowns of trees in a stand.

Clear cutting *See* Extensive clear cutting and Patch clear cutting.

Continuous forest cover A general term covering several silvicultural systems which conserve the local forest canopy/environment during the regeneration phase. Coupe size is normally below 0.25 ha (50 x 50 m) in group systems; and in shelterwood - where used - is retained for longer than 10 years. The general aim of all systems within the concept is the encouragement of diversity of structure and uneven age/size on an intimate scale. (The classical silvicultural system to create continuous forest cover is single tree selection.)

Conversion (= transformation) A change from one silvicultural system to another, usually from clear cutting or coppice systems to alternative systems.

Coupe The individual area of felling; an area of forest which has been felled for regeneration.

Crop A silvicultural or management unit of young trees homogeneous in one or several respects. Later to develop to a stand.

Diverse structure *See* Diversity.

Diversity The use of mixtures or mosaics of different tree species and/or of mixed height/age structure to provide a variety of habitat and continuously varying canopy.

Extensive clear cutting A silvicultural system involving the complete removal of trees before artificial or natural regeneration over extensive areas, ranging from about 30 to 50 ha or more depending on the location and scale of the forest. Felling is usually compressed into a period not exceeding 3 years. No seed trees are retained.

Extraction rack A route created for tending stands and extracting felled trees.

Femelschlag (German) The irregular shelterwood silvicultural system. ('Femel' means 'to select the best'.)

Furetage Use of unregulated fellings in coppice or mixed forest of selection type, thereby improverishing the quality of the stand. (Means 'to rummage'.)

Group (a) An opening or gap made either naturally or by felling; (b) a clump or patch of trees, planted or naturally regenerated.

Irregular (= uneven-aged). Descriptive of a multi-storey structure derived from several regeneration periods on one area with only partial removal of older/larger trees so that multiple canopies are present over a small area. The area of coupe is usually restricted to 0.25 ha (50 x 50 m).

Naturalness The condition produced by nature in balance at a primitive unexploitable stage. Refers to natural processes as well as native species. (Sensitively managed artificial ecosystems using native species can provide valuable wildlife habitats, *simulating* natural ones.)

Normal forest One in which is present an approximately equal area of each age-class up to maturity.

Patch clear cutting An application of the clear cutting system in which coupe size is restricted to about 5-30 ha depending on the location and scale of the forest. No seed trees are retained.

Regular (= even-aged, uniform) Conventionally, uniform extents of forest above 0.25 ha (50 x 50 m).

Restructuring The arrangement and scheduling of fellings and restocking in large even-aged forest so as to introduce more diversity and meet environmental objectives such as a landscape design plan. The felling of some stands is advanced and of others postponed; and coupes are dispersed over the area, usually with a specified interval before adjacent fellings are made. Also applied to an individual stand.

Tending Cleaning, respacing, pruning and thinning operations done in an immature crop in so far as these operations affect the state of the crop and soil at the time of regeneration, and prepare the site for regeneration.

Topex An index of topographic exposure obtained by measuring the angle of inclination to the horizon at eight principal points of the compass; the measurements are used in the windthrow hazard classification to derive estimates of shelter, aspect and funnelling. See Quine and White (1993).

Transformation *See* Conversion.

Silvicultural system The process by which the crops making up a forest are tended, removed and replaced by new crops, resulting in the production of crops of distinctive form.

Stand An area of forest comprising a more or less homogeneous crop in age, species composition and condition. The essential management unit of silviculture.

Windthrow hazard class A classification of hazard ranging from 1 (low) to 6 (high) derived by combining windiness scores (including topex) and soil score for a site. See Miller (1985) and Quine and White (1993).

Wind zone An estimate of regional windiness derived from tatter flags. Site windiness for the windthrow hazard classification is obtained by combining wind zone score with scores representing topographic modifications to the regional windiness, i.e. elevation, topex, aspect and funnelling. See Quine and White (1993).

Glossary 2

Scientific names and authorities of the main English names used in the text

Broadleaves

Ash	*Fraxinus excelsior* L.
Beech	*Fagus sylvatica* L.
Birch, downy	*Betula pubescens* Ehrh.
Birch, silver	*Betula pendula* Roth.
Gean (wild cherry)	*Prunus avium* L.
Hazel	*Corylus avellana* L.
Hornbeam	*Carpinus betulus* L.
Lime, large-leaved	*Tilia platyphyllos* Scop.
Lime, small-leaved	*Tilia cordata* Mill.
Maple, Norway	*Acer platanoides* L.
Oak, pedunculate	*Quercus robur* L.
Oak, sessile	*Quercus petraea* (Mattuschka) Liebl.
Rowan	*Sorbus aucuparia* L.
Sweet chestnut	*Castanea sativa* Mill.
Sycamore	*Acer pseudoplatanus* L.

Conifers

Coast redwood	*Sequoia sempervirens* (D. Don.) Endl.
Corsican pine	*Pinus nigra* var. *maritima* (Ait.) Melville.
Caucasian fir	*Abies nordmanniana* (Stev.) Spach.
Douglas fir	*Pseudotsuga menziesii* (Mirb.) Franco.
European silver fir	*Abies alba* Mill.
Grand fir	*Abies grandis* (Dougl.) Lindl.
Larch, European	*Larix decidua* L.
Larch, Japanese	*Larix kaempferi* (Lamb.) Carr.
Larch, hybrid	*Larix Eurolepis* Henry.
Lodgepole pine, coastal	*Pinus contorta* Dougl. var. *contorta*
Lodgepole pine, inland	*Pinus contorta* Dougl. var. *latifolia* Wats.
Noble fir	*Abies procera* Rehd.
Norway spruce	*Picea abies* (L.) Karst.
Pacific fir	*Abies amabilis* (Dougl.) Forbes
Scots pine	*Pinus sylvestris* L.
Sitka spruce	*Picea sitchensis* (Bong.) Carr.
Wellingtonia	*Sequoiadendron giganteum* (Lindl.) Buchholz.
Western hemlock	*Tsuga heterophylla* (Raf.) Sarg.
Western red cedar	*Thuja plicata* D. Don.

Appendix 1

Classification of silvicultural systems

Source: Matthews (1989)

High forest systems. Crops normally of seedling origin.

Felling and regeneration for the time being concentrated on part of the forest area only:

Old crop cleared by a single felling; resulting crop even-aged – *Clear cutting systems*

Systems of successive regeneration fellings. Old crop cleared by two or more successive fellings; resulting crop more or less even-aged or somewhat uneven-aged:

Regeneration fellings distributed over whole compartments or sub-compartments:

Opening of canopy even; young crops more or less even-aged and uniform – *Uniform systems*

Opening of canopy by scattered gaps; young crop more or less even-aged – *Group system*

Opening of canopy irregular and gradual; young crop somewhat uneven-aged – *Irregular shelterwood system*

Regeneration fellings confined to certain portions of compartments or sub-compartments at a time:

Fellings in strips – *Strip systems*

Fellings beginning in internal lines and advancing outwards in wedge formation – *Wedge system*

Felling and regeneration distributed continuously over the whole area; crop wholly uneven-aged (irregular) – *Selection systems*

Accessory systems arising out of other systems:

Form of forest produced by introducing a young crop beneath an existing immature one – *Two-storied high forest*

Form of forest produced by retaining certain trees of the old crop after regeneration is completed – *High forest with reserves*

Coppice systems. Crops, in part at least, originating from stool shoots (coppice) or by other vegetative means:

Crop consisting entirely of vegetative shoots:

Crop removed by clear felling; even-aged – *Coppice system*

Only a portion of the shoots cut at each felling; crop uneven-aged – *Coppice selection system*

Crop consisting partly of vegetative shoots, partly of trees generally of seedling origin – *Coppice with standards system.*

Appendix 2

Summary of factors to consider in choosing silvicultural systems

In Britain, when contemplating silvicultural systems and their management, the following significant factors or conditions are pertinent.

1. *Scale* State as compared with private forest sector (the latter containing most of the broadleaves). Large-scale as distinct from small-scale application: 90% of private sector woodlands are very small (from 0.1 to 100 ha), while the majority of Forest Enterprise and company forest management units are large or very large (250 to 10 000 ha); the larger the scale the more simplistic is the general silvicultural system adopted.

2. *Objectives* In addition to timber production, landscape, forest recreation potential and wildlife conservation. Where one of the objectives, whatever its ranking, is to create or enhance conditions for sporting and game management or shelter, an uneven-aged system is likely to achieve that objective better than the clear cutting system.

3. *Site conditions* Location, elevation and windthrow hazard class.

   (a) Exposed uplands (above 350 m), mainly in Scotland, Wales and northern and some other parts of England.

   (b) Foothills (200-350 m).

   (c) Lowlands (below 200 m), mainly in England, and in parts of Scotland and Wales.

   This particularly relates to species, terrain, exposure, aspect, climatic conditions and probability of windthrow. Scope for uneven-aged forestry is likely to be greatest in (b) and (c).

4. *Soil types*

   (a) Soils in relation to stability (best in the lowlands).

   (b) Freely drained: brown earths and podzols.

   (c) Imperfectly drained: ironpan soils and podzolic gleys (e.g. upland heaths).

   (d) Inadequately drained: surface-water and peaty gleys and peats (e.g. wet exposed uplands, Wales, the Scottish Borders and West Highlands of Scotland).

   Well-drained soils present the best prospect for uneven-aged forestry.

5. *Animal damage* The likely pressures of deer, grey squirrels, hares and rabbits. The smaller the regeneration unit, the higher are likely to be the costs of protection.

6. *Species and systems*

   (a) Conifers vs broadleaves; pure stands vs mixed stands; mixtures provide greater opportunities for diverse structure and conversion.

   (b) Light-demanding species as opposed to shade-tolerant species; this affects mainly the size of regeneration unit and tolerance of an overstorey.

   (c) Planting as opposed to natural regeneration, coppice regrowth, suckering and direct seeding.

   (d) High forest systems as distinct from coppice systems.

   (e) Stands of even-age as opposed to stands of uneven-age: in even-aged stands the ground usually becomes bare at the end of the rotation, whereas in some uneven-age stands there is prolonged or continuous forest cover which conserves a shrub layer.

(f) Treatment of overstoreys and understoreys of broadleaves (mainly in lowland southern England but including lowlands generally) as distinct from conifers (mainly in uplands).

(g) Special treatment is required (and is available) for ancient and semi-natural woodlands.

7. *Public pressure*, e.g. Lake District in England as compared with Sutherland in Scotland.

The factors outlined relate to the choice of silvicultural system. The practice of any system presupposes at least a general knowledge of the foundations on which silviculture is based, along with some awareness of topics fundamental to many and often to all of them: species, forest ecology, genetics, the use and manipulation of mixtures, the effect of wind, rainfall, disease, insects, mammals and air pollution. Always it is essential to match silvicultural system with sites of different windthrow hazard class. There is a need for adaptability to accommodate prudent changes in forest management.

Appendix 3

Need for research, trials and demonstration areas

In Britain, research into alternative silvicultural systems and stand structures for varied forest types has been infrequent, leaving a major gap in trials and demonstration areas, and restricting experience and training in stand management. The costs and benefits of uneven-aged, diverse structure forestry cannot be fully assessed, or the systems adequately planned or managed without further knowledge and demonstration (Anderson (1953) and Paterson (1958) were foremost among foresters drawing attention to this). In 1980, a Government Select Committee on 'Scientific Aspects of Forestry' received relevant depositions, and recommended diversification of forest 'both in age and composition'. Subsequently, the need for trials and demonstration areas has been advanced by Helliwell (1982, 1985), Pryor and Savill (1986), Paterson (1990), Yorke (1981a,b; 1982, 1992) and the Continuous Cover Forestry Group.

Many aspects of silviculture are common to all types of systems; but there are many differences as to species choice appropriate to the site conditions and climate, the landscaping and conservation objectives, the effects of severe gales, and the problems of damage by insects, diseases and mammals. Systems have to be viable in the prevailing conditions of harvesting and marketing. Nonetheless, basic relevant silvicultural principles which will generally apply to all diverse structure systems include:

- Growing species which will suit the site and climate and predicted markets.

- Using natural regeneration where possible (provided the provenance is acceptable).

- Aiming for structural diversity on as small a scale as is compatible with the species, site and the objectives.

- Causing minimal disturbance to the forest climate and ecological conditions.

- Favouring long rotations.

- Increasing the resistance of the forest to wind.

General requirements of research

Further research, trials and demonstration areas are needed to discover whether a fully convincing economic case can be made for use of alternative systems. Specific requirements of research, particularly in comparing uneven-aged diverse structure systems with the extensive clear cutting system, relate to:

- The respective costs and benefits.

- Variation in timber as to yield, size of assortments, quality and value.

- Costs of regeneration and tending.

- Costs of harvesting. (Harvesting practice needs to accommodate to silviculture.) Costs of sorting mixed species and sizes.

- Costs of management, inventory and supervision. (A plan is advisable to provide continuity of objectives, codified to ensure continuity of management.)

- Damage by mammals, insects and disease. Cost differences of protection, biotic and abiotic.

- Physical and chemical condition of the soil, through time.

- Windthrow incidence. Stability and resistance to storm winds on a stand basis; stem taper, crown and buttress differences.

- Natural regeneration especially factors relating to the effects of different light levels, and of treatments to the soil surface and the forest layer.

- In groups, the effect of shading and competition on the growth of trees and of weeds. Thereupon, to suggest optimum size of groups for all circumstances.

- Non-quantifiable benefits: amenity, internal and external landscape value, nature conservation, 'permanence', soil and water stability and sporting value.

- Mensurational and associated factors. There is need for inventory and periodic measurement of development of structure (Philip, 1994). Often involved will be changes in the way in which trees are selected, marked, felled, extracted and marketed. In the clear cutting system there is a sequence of changes which take place over the length of the rotation, for which adequate Forestry Commission management tables and models are available, but for diverse structure systems there are no such readily available aids (neither for pure stands nor mixtures) and certainly no basis for comparison of silvicultural systems and site conditions. Stem-number curves for various stand types are a possible aid. The *Méthode du Contrôle* or 'Check' method may need to be superseded by a procedure more suited to conditions in Britain, especially for broadleaves: see Philip (1994).

Research on the above would have a strong bearing on improving understanding of the management and economics of uneven-aged diverse structure forest; yet some expected advantages may not be fully proven for many decades. (Current trials are only part way through their planned conversion.) State ownership, offering the best possibility of continuity of management, is ideal for research as well as for trials and demonstration areas. Already, as a result of its multi-purpose objectives, Forest Enterprise is identifying parts of its forest to be managed as permanent structures.

Planning trials and demonstration areas of alternative systems

The need for trials and demonstration areas of alternative systems concerns conifers, broadleaves, and mixed conifers/broadleaves, as suggested hereafter. Starting points could be identification of sites which have the potential for alternative systems, depending upon broad site classes derived from land form, soil type, topex and wind zone; and the development of different practices for each of these.

In conifer forest (mainly uplands)

Paterson (personal communication) suggests several contexts in which the lack of trials and demonstration areas occur, in the uplands:

1. Brown earths on steep slopes: typically in England (the Lakes Forest District), Wales, parts of Scotland (Great Glen, Argyll).
2. Larch and pine stands on upland heaths suitable for:
   (a) natural regeneration by uniform, seed tree or strip systems (this has parallels for lowland pine forests);
   (b) conversion by underplanting to silver firs.
3. Surface-water gleys: peaty and non-peaty:
   (a) large group regeneration (spruce); restricting coupe size and defining size of group for maximum natural regeneration contribution in WHC 4 and 5;
   (b) wedge systems or strip systems (spruce) in WHC 3 and 4; stand preparation; dimensions.
4. Moraine-peat complex (West and North Highlands and Galloway): restructuring; restricting coupe size; and exploring use of moraine sites for stabilising coupe margins and for species component mix.
5. Moorland sites: conversion from lodgepole pine.
6. Lower slopes (i.e. sites 'lower down the hill'), ex-agricultural.

Paterson (personal communication) further emphasises the need to marry landscape objectives to the silvicultural systems necessary to achieve them. Of significant interest is to know (particularly for landscape reasons) the stability of margins and the matrix left between initial coupes in WHC 5 and 6, gley/peat/peaty ironpan soil zones (and even in WHC 4, gley/brown earth zones). Landscape design plans appear to envisage margins lasting for at least 10 years; if they do not – as is expected – other stand treatments will have to be devised. Work on severance thinning below critical height may be involved.

Examples of strip and wedge systems for regeneration of Sitka spruce and Norway spruce are rare on locally more sheltered gleys (an exception is the attempt at Fernworthy on Dartmoor in England). Further experience is needed to define widths and techniques in more windy climates.

Empirical practice in alternative systems appears to arise to meet defined recreational and landscape objectives of Forest Enterprise in or beside Forest Parks, for example: Douglas fir group regeneration and larch at Whinlatter, in the Lakes Forest District; Sitka spruce natural regeneration in coupes of 10-12 ha strip uniform shelterwood in Hamsterley beside Northumberland Park; and small coupes for natural regeneration in Douglas fir at Coed y Brenin in Wales. Research into public preferences could provide guidance to the forester for the management of areas much used for recreation including urban conifer woodland.

Paterson (personal communication) further suggests that it would be venturesome for Forest Enterprise, in association with the Forestry Commission, to identify moderately sized blocks larger than Glentress (117 ha), of about P45-P65 in some of the site contexts suggested above and to begin to manage them in co-operative plans with the Research Division, exploring group size, group conversion, stand preparation for regeneration, underplanting and natural regeneration, as appropriate. The Northern Research Station has unique opportunities to monitor large-scale demonstrations of alternative systems on various forest/site types. The range is expressed by Paterson (1990): see Table 8.1. The wide territorial distribution of the Forestry Commission research outstations forms a useful network to cover the necessary monitoring. Possible options for large scale research demonstrations of alternative silvicultural systems for conifers on various forest/site types in upland state forests given by Paterson (1990, amended) are included in Appendix 4 of this Bulletin. This is long-term work; a commitment by all parties concerned needs to be envisaged over 15-30 years at least.

An important benefit of engaging in studies of stand structure would be that several scientific teams could co-operate around them to study effects of lateral shelter on growth, deer control problems, internal and external landscape quality, intensity of pine weevil and black pine beetle damage, and the benefits for wildlife and vegetation compared with similar areas treated under the clear cutting system. Information on stability and wind behaviour in various stand structures would fill an important gap, as Britain's wind climate is so different from that on the Continent of Europe. Operational economics could also be studied by the Technical Branch of the Forestry Commission.

Publication would be welcomed of the results from Neustein's series of Forestry Commission experiments (see Chapter 3) on strip shelterwood and conversion by underplanting Scots pine and larch stands in both the littoral sand sites and some other better status larch sites, using Douglas fir, Norway spruce and *Abies* spp. This does not detract from the need for setting up contemporary working examples distributed around Britain and including some site types not covered adequately by the experiments of that period, e.g. moraine/peat complex, lodgepole pine conversion, and upland spruce on WHC 5 and 6.

In broadleaved forest (mainly lowlands)

Helliwell (1982, 1985) and Pryor (1985, 1990) have made relevant suggestions regarding management of alternative systems for broadleaves. The use of quite small groups may be adequate for beech but not for light-demanding broadleaves. Useful work could be undertaken as to the edge shade tolerance of oak and other light-demanding species on different aspects in treeshelter experiments which could lead to definition of appropriate group sizes. Suitable methods for utilising the interplay of regeneration of ash and sycamore also need to be explored and seem likely to be some form of group regeneration and group structure (Waters and Savill, 1992). Bowhill and Eildon (in south central Scotland), Ebworth (on the Cotswolds) and other stands (in southern England) provide examples of group selection experience in broadleaved woodland.

The need for trials and demonstration areas on lowland broadleaved forest (Evans, 1984) are only different for the uplands by the presence of extensive over-grazed semi-natural birchwoods and less extensive upland oakwoods. In Wales, initiatives for oakwoods, concerning group size with or without seed trees, are being discussed by the Forestry Commission and Coed Cymru, addressing appropriate silvicultural systems for western semi-natural oakwoods. It would have to be demonstrated that small group regeneration for old degraded oakwoods can be successful. Birch in Scotland seems flexible to several approaches — uniform seed tree, strip felling or group regeneration — and may not merit research effort after protection is achieved from sheep grazing and deer browsing and bark-stripping.

Appendix 4

Suggestions for trials and demonstration areas

Possible options for large scale research demonstrations of alternative silvicultural systems for conifers on various forest/site types in upland State forests (Paterson, 1990, amended)

Country	Forest location	Species	System trial	Research centre
Scotland	Ae	Sitka spruce	(a) Group regeneration	Mabie
	Solway, Ae	Sitka spruce	(b) Wedge/strip felling	Mabie
	Wauchope	Sitka spruce Sitka spruce/lodgepole pine	(a) Group regeneration WHC 5	Bush
	Argyll	Sitka spruce/Norway spruce	(a) Wedge/strip felling WHC 3	Cairnbaan
	Glengarry or Shin (moorland)	Sitka spruce/lodgepole pine	(a) Conversion of lodgepole pine, even-aged and snow-damaged plantations	Newton
	Ichnacardoch (Lon Mor)	Mixed conifers (mainly lodgepole pine, Sitka spruce and Scots pine)	(a) Group structure Anderson	Newton
	Inshriach	Larches, Scots pine	(a) Uniform seed tree natural regeneration	Newton
	Speymouth	Scots pine	(a) Strip felling	Newton
	Tummel (Forest Park)	Larches, Scots pine	(a) Conversion by underplanting with Douglas fir, beech, Pacific fir, Norway spruce	Perth/Bush
	Montreathmont (Angus lowlands)	Scots pine	(a) Conversion by underplanting (b) Uniform seed tree natural regeneration	Perth/Bush
	Tummel (Faskally) (Craigvinean)	Douglas fir, larches, Scots pine, oak, beech	(a) Maintain conversion to small group diverse structure	Perth/Bush
Wales	Brechfa	Larches	(a) Conversion to Douglas fir, Pacific fir, beech	Talybont
	Coed y Brenin	Douglas fir, Japanese larch	(a) Group regeneration Douglas fir, maple	Talybont
	Twyi Brecon	Sitka spruce	(a) Group and strip regeneration WHC 3 and 4	Talybont
England	Hamsterley	Sitka spruce/Scots pine	(a) Group regeneration	Kielder
	Kielder	Sitka spruce	(a) Group regeneration WHC 5	Kielder
	Newcastleton	Norway spruce/Sitka spruce	(a) Wedge/strip felling WHC 3 and 4	Kielder

Appendix 5

History and Personalities

In Scotland, the first extensive planting by the improving landowners of avenue and park trees, shelterbelts and policy woods for chiefly non-wood benefits took place mainly between 1810 and 1865, financed by profits from farming, cotton, coal-mining, rents and town property development. These were predominantly even-aged broadleaved and mixed woods situated in the lowlands and lower foothills, woods which often have the potential for continuous forest cover. This period and continuing up to 1910 was also when improving lairds (such as Seafield and Atholl) used their estate and other revenues to plant extensively Scots pine, European larch and Norway spruce for timber production. Some pine stands in the Spey and Dee Valleys were naturally regenerated by the uniform shelterwood system until emergency clear cutting during World Wars I and II (1914-18 and 1939-45) terminated the use of such silvicultural systems. The Caithness policy woodlands, based on sycamore and beech, were perhaps the last of the policy or shelterwoods, dating from about 1890-1910. Shelter was very important there, but was also a common objective elsewhere to protect farm crops and livestock. There has been interest in finding ways of renewing these woods and belts without clear cutting in order to maintain amenity and shelter. In 1926 the Duke of Buccleuch at Bowhill, near Selkirk, and Eildon, near Melrose, started a group selection system in broadleaves and conifers within his policy woods.

In England, meanwhile, management of the depleted Crown forests was transferred in 1810 from the Surveyor-General of Woods to the Commissioners of Woods and Forests ('The Office of Woods'). Sporadic planting, and somewhat uninspired management, occurred in the Forest of Dean and the New Forest until in 1923 the Forestry Commission accepted responsibility (James, 1981). In the private sector during the 19th century some private woodland owners continued to give attention to game management and shooting, but also showed an increasing interest in growing exotic conifers for timber. Much private planting took place in many counties including Cumberland, Devon, Durham and Lincolnshire. However, there are no indications of use of alternative silvicultural systems to clear cutting.

In Britain, the first sustained stage in the development of uneven-aged forest was moderately stimulated by foresters in the Forest of Dean from 1896 (Everard, 1992), and by Schlich and Troup in the 1920s. From the early 1900s, the Coke family of Norfolk, in their Weasenham New Wood, had begun a selection system in conifers (front cover plate). Subsequently, there have been several contributions—notably those of Anderson, Bourne, Garfitt, Penistan, Hiley, Paterson and Reade—to advocate silvicultural systems alternative to clear cutting. Among later practitioners have been Lord Bradford, Hutt, McHardy, Everard, Workman, Yorke and Pryor.

Mark L. Anderson. From 1929, notable encouragement of uneven-aged systems was given by M.L. Anderson (born 1895, died 1961; Plate 24) who, after graduating from the University of Edinburgh in 1919 joined the newly appointed Forestry Commission and became a research officer. Later, he served as Director of the Forest Service in Eire, lecturer in the University of Oxford and, from 1951 to 1961, Professor of Forestry in the University of Edinburgh. He was steeped in the literature of Continental forestry, and his varied experience of silviculture in western and central Europe and Scandinavia gave authority to his teaching and publications. In particular, his preparation of the English editions of silvicultural texts by Knüchel (1953) and Köstler (1956) made two detailed accounts of Continental silviculture available to English-speaking foresters.

Anderson (1953) pointed out that, in consequence of British foresters' concentration on creating and managing forest on the clear cutting even-aged system, 'there has been little appreciation of the importance of the stand and the site, considered *together* as a single producing agent and not separately, and of the need for maintaining the production of that combination in perpetuity, or even of increasing it ... [and] instead of a perennial stand we have aimed at a succession of crop following crop with no clear idea of whether these crops are better or worse than their predecessors'. He asserted that Britain's 'silviculture can be improved only by experience. It cannot be standardised or made stereotyped, because in this country we have a very wide variety of conditions and we are devoting our energies to the growing of a great variety of tree species, often influenced by the whims and vagaries of a number of rather inexperienced experts. All this leads to a great deal of confusion, largely because we do not make use of some simple method of assessing results, which would at least tell us what is happening within our woodlands as a result of the various treatments that we apply to them. The time factor does militate, of course, against the proper study of treatment effects, because any such study, to be of real value, must be carried on for quite a long period of years.' Anderson (1953) further asserted that 'progress in forest management and silvicultural practice in this country cannot be made until we adopt some method of readily determining the effects upon production of the various techniques and treatments we apply'. He advocated the adoption of the *Méthode du Contrôle* (which he termed the 'standing control' or 'standing check' method) especially for all woodland areas which it is proposed to run as uneven-aged forest, to assess and control the growing-stock on a wide scale, and to enable forest owners and foresters to obtain reliable knowledge of what is really

Plate 24. *Professor Mark Louden Anderson MC MA DSc FRSE (1895–1961)*

happening to their growing-stock or forest capital.

Anderson (1960) subsequently presented a thorough analysis of the climatic and site conditions prevailing in the Vosges, Jura, Alps and Carpathians where mixed forests of Norway spruce, European silver fir and beech are managed under the single tree selection system. He speculated whether similar forest could be reproduced by planting in certain parts of Scotland, particularly at the higher elevations where exposure is severe. He concluded that parts of the uplands of east-central and south-central Scotland with severe winters and moderate though well-distributed rainfall would provide suitable sites, especially if the soils were derived from rocks of Upper Silurian age in south Scotland and hornblende schists in the Highlands. Anderson further suggested that group selection would be the most suitable system. He proposed that dense groups of birch, larch and alder, spaced quite widely, should be established to suppress the ground vegetation and to provide shelter for the later planting of spruce, European silver fir, sycamore and other broadleaved species between the spaced groups in a progressive development towards an uneven-aged structure. Between 1929 and 1932 he designed trials of a method of planting densely stocked, well-separated, small groups of conifers on upland sites being afforested in Scotland and northern England (Anderson, 1930, 1931, 1951). Although the second stage was never planted, the trials showed that a diverse forest structure could be achieved by planting conifers in groups arranged in systematic fashion. The system did not become popular practice because of the slow build-up of production and the risk of browse damage to any secondary planting done between groups from deer using the cover of the groups, and the fact that the external trees in these so-called 'Anderson Groups' grew faster than the central ones, thus suppressing them, and the survivors were coarsely branched. The aim of these small groups was also to concentrate ground preparation on a fraction of the area. Anderson (1967) recorded the following additional relevant comments on alternative silvicultural systems in Britain:

[In the late 1920s] 'while the State [Forest] service was still pondering over [clear cutting], the new teachings of the Swiss school of Biolley and others were having their effects. These were against clear-felling methods and in favour of selection or uneven-aged forest, especially for hilly regions. Ponsonby (1931), who had been an Irish representative on the Forestry Commission, and who owned a wooded property in County Tipperary, wrote an important article called 'A System of Forestry for the British Isles', advocating a departure from the pure even-aged stand to selection working. In this he had the support of Major [the Honourable Richard] Coke who successfully applied such a method to his Norfolk estate [at Weasenham]. The challenge was taken up by A. C. Forbes and a lively

discussion went on for a year or two, in the course of which Ponsonby, answering criticisms about going abroad for guidance, asked had we not brought over, naturalised and knighted Sir William Schlich (1840-1925) in order to teach us the lessons of Continental forestry? And do we not go abroad to study the subject? In due course, on the basis of Continental experience, [R.] Bourne in England spread the new gospel and his colleague, [M.J.] Penistan, during his stay in the south of Scotland as a Forestry Commission officer, found many disciples on private estates. In 1950 Penistan wrote in favour of methods of natural regeneration and claimed that mixed woods were easier to manage. In 1952 he was suggesting alternative methods [to] extensive clear-felling, and described improvement of woods in Dumfries and Galloway. In 1949, Urquhart also came out in favour of uneven structure. In 1953, [W.N.] Gibson sounded a warning against even-aged structure, pointing out that there were more pure stands than in the past. Gaps caused by windfalls would result in irregular stands. By 1960, Edinburgh University Forestry Department had initiated six large-scale long-term experiments in the conversion of even-aged stands [into] a group structure with the co-operation of the Forestry Commission and four private forest owners. There was a growing appreciation that silvicultural treatment must be varied for species other than light-demanders.'

Anderson's further applications have been noted in Chapter 3. He did not favour either underplanting or two-storied high forest; he was relieved that by 1960 they had 'not invaded Scotland'. [However, they had occurred. Morley Penistan and Frank Oliver during 1945-60 encouraged the underplanting of larch stands in East Scotland, not with a view to two-storied high forest but as a means of reducing weeding costs and frost damage to more productive successor species (such as Noble fir, grand fir, western hemlock, Douglas fir and Norway spruce) which do not establish well in open extensive clear cutting in the semi-Continental climate over the regions of Tayside and Grampian owing to such factors as frost and May drought.] In the 1960s the Forestry Commission Research and Development established large underplanting experiments in Drumtochty, Michaelston Drummond Hill, Allerston, Coed Morgannwg, Culbin and Radnor.

Ray Bourne. Bourne (born 1889, died 1949) one of Sir William Schlich's students, was the first forester to practise in Britain variants of the selection system and to apply the *Méthode du Contrôle*. He was appointed to the Indian Forest Service in 1911. From 1922 to 1937 he lectured in forest management at the University of Oxford. He then resigned to become a consultant to private woodlands. His extensive knowledge of Continental silviculture and forest management was passed on to students in lectures and during study tours in Germany, France and Switzerland as well as to a wide audience of professional foresters (Bourne, 1945, 1951; Hiley, 1964). Bourne 'took neglected and semi-neglected woodlands, extracted revenue from them, filled them with natural regeneration, and progressively improved the growing stock in volume and still more in value. It was a highly personal form of management, and he appreciated the point of criticism that it would be much more difficult for a successor to take over such work than if it had been organised on more orthodox lines' (Steven, 1948). Bourne (1951) began from the mid-1920s to convert several stands of beech-woods in the Chilterns to a variant of selection forest, which treatment resulted in an increased range of diameter classes and an increase in volume of the growing stock. Regeneration of ash was adequate but that of beech and oak were lacking.

J. E. Garfitt. Ted Garfitt succeeded to Ray Bourne's consultancy practice. He had studied under Bourne at Oxford before joining the Malayan Forest Service in 1936, where he had five years' experience in the management of tropical rain forest on a sustained yield basis until this was interrupted by the Japanese invasion. This type of management had a strong group basis since natural regeneration of the large species of dipterocarps tended in this direction. After 1945, Garfitt continued the work initiated by Bourne on a number of lowland private estates and also developed his own *ad hoc* methods of group selection on the war devastated broadleaved woodlands at Cirencester Park, Gloucestershire. These provided an ideal form of management for application to unproductive or unmanaged broadleaved woodlands in lowland England (Garfitt, 1953, 1963, 1966, 1977, 1979, 1980, 1984, 1987, 1988, 1995). They provided the opportunity to grow both shade-tolerant and light-demanding species, with all the advantages of the group selection system. Garfitt continued this work on estates, wherever the conditions proved suitable and practicable, for a period of 40 years until his retirement in 1987. His group selection system and some of his applications have been noted in Chapter 3.

M. J. Penistan. Morley Penistan (born 1914, died 1986), a one time Forestry Commission Conservator, was an enthusiastic advocate of uneven-aged forestry. He had studied under Ray Bourne and was familiar with the work of M.L. Anderson. His interest in this type of forestry in both England and Scotland increased following an extensive tour of forests in France, Belgium and Germany in 1956 (Penistan, 1960, 1968, 1974). During a visit by the then Society of Foresters of Great Britain to the Belgian Ardennes, which he helped to organise, attention was drawn to Turner's (1959) method of converting uniform stands of Norway spruce to a diverse structure of mixed species in clearings. Penistan recognised its potential and advocated its adoption in plantations of Norway spruce and Sitka spruce to diversify the structure of upland forests in Britain.

M. G. Reade DSC. Michael Reade, another forester who recognised the potential of variants of Continental diverse structure systems in British conditions, has consistently practised since the 1950s what he terms 'irregular selection forest' or 'irregular shelterwood' in Chiltern beechwoods on his Ipsden Estate in Oxfordshire. He wrote descriptions of the systems as they were being practised in Switzerland at that time (Reade, 1957, 1960, 1965, 1990). His application has been noted in Chapter 4.

Printed in the United Kingdom for HMSO
Dd 0297433 C23 11/95 552 12521